Target 5
Get back on track

Edexcel GCSE (9–1)
English Literature

Unseen Poetry

David Grant

Pearson

Published by Pearson Education Limited, 80 Strand, London, WC2R ORL.
www.pearsonschoolsandfecolleges.co.uk

Text © Pearson Education Ltd 2017
Typeset by Tech-Set Ltd, Gateshead

The right of David Grant to be identified as author of this work has been asserted by him in accordance with the Copyright, Designs
and Patents Act 1988.

First published 2017

20 19 18 17
10 9 8 7 6 5 4 3 2 1

British Library Cataloguing in Publication Data
A catalogue record for this book is available from the British Library

ISBN 978 1 292 23013 9

Printed in Slovakia by Neografia

Acknowledgments
Pages 2, 4, 5, 6: 'Tea' from *Love Poems* by Carol Ann Duffy. Copyright © 2010. Used by permission of Pan Macmillan; pages 10,
11, 12, 13: 'maggie and milly and molly and may' from *Complete Poems*, 1904–1962 by e e Cummings, edited by George J. Firmage.
Copyright © 1956, 1984, 1991 by the Trustees of the e e Cummings Trust. Used by permission of Liveright Publishing Corporation;
page 18: 'Otherwise' from *Collected Poems* by Jane Kenyon. Copyright © 2005 by the Estate of Jane Kenyon. Reprinted with the
permission of The Permissions Company, Inc. on behalf of Graywolf Press, Minneapolis, Minnesota. www.graywolfpress.org; pages
26, 27, 28: 'City Lilacs' from *Glad of These Times* by Helen Dunmore. Copyright © 2007. Reproduced with permission of Bloodaxe
Books. www.bloodaxebooks.com; pages 34, 35, 36: 'The Round' from *Passing Through: The Later Poems – New and Selected* by
Stanley Kunitz. Copyright © 1985. Used by permission of W. W. Norton & Company, Inc.; pages 42, 43, 44, 47: 'Postcard' by
Beatrice Garland. Copyright © Beatrice Garland; pages 50, 51, 52, 54: 'Strawberries' from *New Selected Poems* by Edwin Morgan.
Copyright © 2000. Used by permission of Carcanet Press; pages 58, 59, 60: 'My Grandfather's Garden' from *The Blue Book* by
Owen Sheers (Seren, 2000); pages 58, 59, 60: 'Poem' from *The Shout: Selected Poems* by Simon Armitage. Copyright © Simon
Armitage; page 74: 'Legend' from *Five Fields* by Gillian Clarke. Copyright © 1998. Used by permission of Carcanet Press; page 75:
'Mother to Son' from *The Collected Poems of Langston Hughes* by Langston Hughes, edited by Arnold Rampersad with David
Roessel, Associate Editor. Copyright © 1994 by the Estate of Langston Hughes. Used by permission of Alfred A. Knopf, an imprint
of the Knopf Doubleday Publishing Group, a division of Penguin Random House LLC. All rights reserved; Reprinted by permission of
Harold Ober Associates Incorporated. Copyright © 1994 by the Estate of Langston Hughes; page 76: 'A Letter in October' from
Weather Central by Ted Kooser, © 1994. Reprinted by permission of the University of Pittsburgh Press.

Note from the publisher
Pearson has robust editorial processes, including answer and fact checks, to ensure the accuracy of the content in this publication,
and every effort is made to ensure this publication is free of errors. We are, however, only human, and occasionally errors do occur.
Pearson is not liable for any misunderstandings that arise as a result of errors in this publication, but it is our priority to ensure that
the content is accurate. If you spot an error, please do contact us at resourcescorrections@pearson.com so we can make sure it is
corrected.

Contents

① Tackling an unseen poem

This unit will help you to read, understand and explore an unseen poem. The skills you will build are to:

- read and develop an understanding of an unseen poem
- identify the key ideas in the poem
- identify the poet's intention – the impact the poet wants their poem to have on a reader.

In the exam you will face a question like the one below. At the end of the unit you will **write one paragraph** in response to this question, focusing on **one of these poems**: *Tea*, on the next page. You will then have an opportunity to explore the second poem and compare them both.

> **Exam-style question**
>
> Compare the ways the writers present love in *Tea* and *When You Are Old*.
>
> In your answer you should compare:
> - the ideas in the poems
> - the poets' use of language
> - the poets' use of form and structure.
>
> Use **evidence** from the poems to support your **comparison**.   (20 marks)

Before you respond to the question you will work through three key questions in the **skills boosts** to help you tackle an unseen poem.

① **How do I read a poem and check my understanding?**	② **How do I identify the key ideas in a poem?**	③ **How do I identify the poet's intention?**

Read the poem on the next page. In Paper 2, Section B, Part 2 of your English Literature exam, you will compare **two** unseen poems.

As you read the poem, think about: ⊘

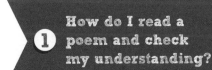

who is talking to whom

what they are saying

why they are saying it.

Tea 🖉

I like pouring your tea, lifting
the heavy pot, and tipping it up,
so the fragrant liquid streams in your china cup.

Or when you're away, or at work,
5   I like to think of your cupped hands as you sip,
as you sip, of the faint half-smile of your lips.

I like the questions – sugar? – milk? –
and the answers I don't know by heart, yet,
for I see your soul in your eyes, and I forget.

10   Jasmine, Gunpowder, Assam, Earl Grey, Ceylon,
I love tea's names. Which tea would you like? I say
but it's any tea for you, please, any time of day,

as the women harvest the slopes
for the sweetest leaves, on Mount Wu-Yi,
15   and I am your lover, smitten, straining your tea.

Carol Ann Duffy

(1) Underline (A) any words or phrases in the poem that you do not recognise or understand.

(2) You can often work out the meaning of unfamiliar words or phrases by looking at words or phrases around them. Look at the circled phrases from the poem, below.

A   Jasmine, Gunpowder, Assam, Earl Grey, Ceylon,
I love tea's names. Which tea would you like? I say

B   as the women harvest the slopes
for the sweetest leaves, on Mount Wu-Yi,

(a) Note 🖉 down alongside each circled phrase everything that you can work out about its meaning.

(b) Underline (A) other words or phrases around them that helped you.

(3) Look again at any of the words or phrases you underlined in the poem because you did not recognise or understand them. Note 🖉 down alongside them what you can work out about their meaning by looking at other words and phrases around them.

If you're still not sure about an idea or a phrase or a word in an unseen poem, work around it – focus on what you <u>do</u> understand.

How do I read a poem and check my understanding?

When you first read a poem that you have never seen before, you need to read it carefully and be confident that you have understood what it is about.

Read the poem *Tea* on page 2 again.

Always read the poem **twice**.

One way to develop your understanding of a poem is to picture in your mind what is being described.

① **a** Read the first verse of the poem. Picture the scene in your mind, then draw 🖉 that picture in the space below. You can use:

- stick people with expressions on their faces
- speech bubbles and thought bubbles
- labels to make your drawing clearer.

b Look at your drawing. Write 🖉 **one** sentence, summarising the poem.

c Re-read the poem, checking each line and each verse against your summary of the poem. Is your summary accurate? Annotate 🖉 your summary with any changes needed to make it more accurate.

d Circle Ⓐ **two** key words or phrases in the poem on page 2 that support, and help to explain, your summary.

② How do I identify the key ideas in a poem?

Focusing on the writer's vocabulary choices, the title and the poem's final line, can help you to identify, and develop your understanding of, the poem's key ideas.

① The **title** of a poem and its **final line** often give clear clues to the key ideas in the poem.

Look at the title and the final line of the poem *Tea* on page 2. What do you think are the key ideas in the poem?

a Note 🖉 the key ideas below, using just **one** or **two** words to sum up each idea.

....

....

b Label 🖉 each key idea you have identified **A, B, C**, etc.

② Now look at all the nouns, verbs, adjectives and adverbs the writer has used in the poem.

	✓	🖉		✓	🖉		✓	🖉		✓	🖉
answers			half-smile			milk			straining		
Assam			hands			Mount Wu-Yi			streams		
Ceylon			harvest			names			sugar		
china			heart			please			sweetest		
cup			heavy			pot			tea		
cupped			Jasmine			pouring			think		
day			know			questions			time		
Earl Grey			leaves			say			tipping		
eyes			lifting			see			women		
faint			lips			sip			work		
forget			liquid			slopes					
fragrant			love			smitten					
Gunpowder			lover			soul					

a Tick ✓ each word that is linked to the key ideas you noted in question **① a** above.

b Look at all the words you have ticked. Label 🖉 each one with the letter you gave to the relevant key idea in question **① b** above.

③ a Now highlight 🖉 all the pronouns (e.g. 'I', 'you', 'he', 'she', etc...) that the writer has used in the poem and list 🖉 them below in the order in which they occur.

....

b Look at all the pronouns you noted above. Which one does the poet use most? Which is the next most common? What does this suggest about the poem's key ideas? Write 🖉 **two** or **three** sentences on paper summing up your understanding of the poem's key ideas.

3 How do I identify the poet's intention?

Identifying the poet's intention will help you to develop your understanding and explore how the poet has tried to achieve that intention.

> intention: the impact that the writer wants the text to have on the reader

① Identifying the characters in a poem – all the people the poet writes about and the ways in which these characters interact – can help your understanding of the poem and the poet's intention. Look again at *Tea* on page 2.

   ⓐ Who are the people in this poem? Label ✎ the diagram below.

   ⓑ Who is talking to whom? Add ✎ **one** or **more** speech bubbles to the diagram with a summary of what they are saying.

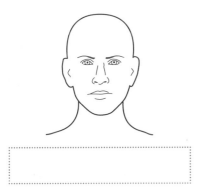

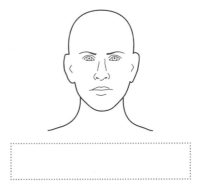

② Look carefully at these key lines from the poem.

> I like the questions – sugar? – milk? –
> and the answers I don't know by heart, yet,
> for I see your soul in your eyes, and I forget.

What impressions does the poet want the reader to have about each of the people in the poem and what they are talking about? Add ✎ your ideas to the diagram above.

③ Review the diagram above. What are your thoughts, feelings and impressions of these people? How do you think the writer wants you to think and feel about them? Write ✎ **one** or **two** sentences summing up your ideas about the writer's intention.

....

....

....

....

....

Tackling an unseen poem

When you begin to tackle an unseen poem, aim to:

- 'picture the poem': imagine the scene or events the poet is writing about
- look at the title, the final line, and the writer's vocabulary choices, to help you identify the key ideas in the poem
- think about your impressions of the people and ideas in the poem to help you identify the writer's intention.

Now look at this exam-style question you saw at the start of the unit.

Exam-style question

Compare the ways the writers present love in *Tea* and *When You Are Old*.

In your answer you should compare:
- the ideas in the poems
- the poets' use of language
- the poets' use of form and structure.

Use **evidence** from the poems to support your **comparison**.   (20 marks)

(1) Circle Ⓐ the key words in the exam-style question above: what are you being asked to write about?

(2) Which of the student's ideas in the planning notes below would you include in your response? Tick ✓ them.

A ☐	I like pouring your tea	*The speaker likes making tea for the person she loves.*
B ☐	when you're away, or at work I like to think of your cupped hands as you sip	*She often thinks about this person when they're not there.*
C ☐	the answers I don't know by heart, yet	*She hasn't known this person long but expects them to be together for a long time.*
D ☐	it's any tea for you, please, any time of day	*This person loves tea.*
E ☐	Jasmine, Gunpowder, Assam, Earl Grey, Ceylon	*She loves the names of different teas.*
F ☐	I am your lover, smitten, straining your tea	*She has very strong feelings for this person. She enjoys doing things that make this person happy.*
G ☐	I see your soul in your eyes, and I forget.	*Her feelings are so strong that they stop her thinking about anything else.*

Your turn!

You are now going to write **one paragraph** in response to the exam-style question, **summarising the key ideas** and **the writer's intention** in *Tea* by Carol Ann Duffy **only**.

Exam-style question

Compare the ways the writers present love in *Tea* and *When You Are Old*.

In your answer you should compare:
* the ideas in the poems
* the poets' use of language
* the poets' use of form and structure.

Use **evidence** from the poems to support your **comparison**.   (20 marks)

(1) Look back through all your work in this unit. Use the space below to note 🖉 all the thoughts and ideas you could include in your summary.

The key ideas in the poem	The impressions that the writer wants to give of the people in the poem

(2) Which of the ideas you have noted are relevant to the exam-style question? Highlight 🖉 them.

(3) Using your notes, write **one** paragraph on paper in response to the exam-style question above, **summarising the key ideas** and **the writer's intention** in *Tea* by Carol Ann Duffy.

Review your skills

Check up

Review your response to the exam-style question on page 7. Tick ✓ the column to show how well you think you have done each of the following.

	Not quite ✓	Nearly there ✓	Got it! ✓
summarised the key ideas in the poem	☐	☐	☐
summarised the writer's intention	☐	☐	☐

Need more practice?

Look again at the exam-style question you have been working on in this unit.

Exam-style question

Compare the ways the writers present love in *Tea* and *When You Are Old*.

In your answer you should compare:
- the ideas in the poems
- the poets' use of language
- the poets' use of form and structure.

Use **evidence** from the poems to support your **comparison**. (20 marks)

Now read *When You Are Old* by William Butler Yeats which can be found on page 73. When you have read it twice,
- 'picture the poem': imagine the scene or events the poet is writing about
- look at the title, the final line and the writer's vocabulary choices, to help you identify the key ideas in the poem
- think about your impressions of the people and ideas in the poem to help you identify the writer's intention.

Write **one** paragraph in response to the exam-style question, focusing on *When You Are Old* by William Butler Yeats. Aim to **summarise** the poem's key ideas and the writer's intention. You'll find some suggested points to refer to in the Answers section.

Comparison practice

Write ✏ **one** or **two** paragraphs in response to the exam-style question, **comparing** the key ideas and the writers' intentions in *Tea* **and** *When You Are Old*. You'll find some suggested points to refer to in the Answers section.

How confident do you feel about each of these **skills**? Colour ✏ in the bars.

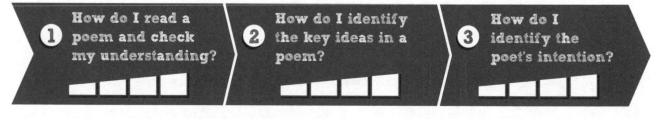

1 How do I read a poem and check my understanding?

2 How do I identify the key ideas in a poem?

3 How do I identify the poet's intention?

② Developing a personal response

This unit will help you to develop a personal response to an unseen poem. The skills you will build are to:

- develop your response to the ideas in an unseen poem
- identify and explore the mood of an unseen poem
- develop confidence in your response to an unseen poem.

In the exam you will face a question like the one below. At the end of the unit you will **write two paragraphs** in response to this question, focusing on **one of these poems**: *maggie and milly and molly and may*, on the next page. You will then have an opportunity to explore the second poem and compare them both.

Exam-style question

Compare the ways the writers present childhood in *maggie and milly and molly and may* and *Legend*.

In your answer you should compare:
- the ideas in the poems
- the poets' use of language
- the poets' use of form and structure.

Use **evidence** from the poems to support your **comparison**.   (20 marks)

Before you tackle the question you will work through three key questions in the **skills boosts** to help you develop a personal response to the poem.

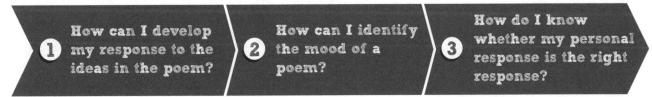

① How can I develop my response to the ideas in the poem?

② How can I identify the mood of a poem?

③ How do I know whether my personal response is the right response?

Read the poem on the next page. In Paper 2, Section B, Part 2 of your English Literature exam, you will compare **two** unseen poems.

As you read the poem, think about: ⊘

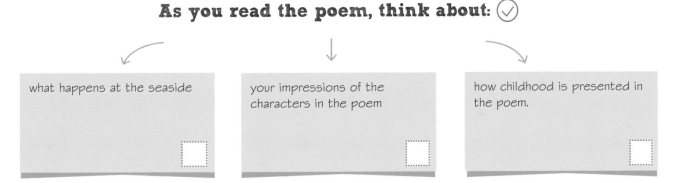

what happens at the seaside	your impressions of the characters in the poem	how childhood is presented in the poem.
☐	☐	☐

> ### maggie and milly and molly and may
>
> maggie and milly and molly and may
> went down to the beach (to play one day)
>
> and maggie discovered a shell that sang
> so sweetly she couldn't remember her troubles, and
>
> 5 milly befriended a stranded star
> whose rays five languid fingers were;
>
> and molly was chased by a horrible thing
> which raced sideways while blowing bubbles: and
>
> may came home with a smooth round stone
> 10 as small as a world and as large as alone.
>
> For whatever we lose (like a you or a me)
> it's always ourselves we find in the sea
>
> e e cummings

(1) When you first read a poem, think about:
- **what** happens
- **when** and/or **where** it happens
- **who** is in the poem
- **how** the events, places and people in the poem are presented.

(a) Imagine the scene described in the poem. What is the poem about? Note 🖉 down all your ideas below.

(b) Write 🖉 **one** or **two** sentences summarising your ideas. You could begin your summary:

| The poem is about... | The poem explores... | The poem focuses on... |

How can I develop my response to the ideas in the poem?

When you have read a poem, read through it again, thinking about and responding to each idea and image it creates in your mind. Then, to help you develop your response, **think about how those ideas and images can be connected.**

(1) Look at the image created in the **first** stanza of the poem.

> maggie and milly and molly and may
> went down to the beach (to play one day)

What does this first image lead you to expect from the poem? Annotate ✐ the quotation above with your ideas.

(2) Now look at some more images and ideas taken from the poem.

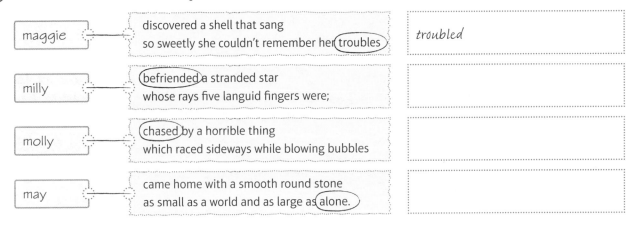

Look carefully at what happens to each character in the poem and each of the words the poet has selected to describe those events. What might the poet be suggesting about each character? Note ✐ **one** or **two** words alongside each quotation. One idea has been suggested for you.

(3) Poems often connect very different ideas, settings, people or events to make you think about them in a different way.

What connections can you make between the ways in which the writer presents the setting, characters and events in the poem? Are there any strange or surprising connections?

Write ✐ **one** or **two** sentences explaining your ideas.

> Try comparing what the first stanza of the poem leads you to expect, with the rest of the poem.

....

....

....

Unit 2 Developing a personal response   **11**

2 How can I identify the mood of a poem?

Certain key words can create the mood of a poem.

mood: the emotion, tone or atmosphere created in a text

When you think about the mood of a poem, or part of a poem:

• decide whether the mood is positive or negative

• try to think of a more specific word that describes the mood as precisely as possible.

For example, the mood might be:

positive

| optimistic | affectionate | comic | warm | contemplative | sympathetic | happy | excited |

negative

| pessimistic | gloomy | disturbing | unsettling | terrifying | cynical | angry | tense |

(1) Think about the mood suggested at the **start** of the poem on page 10.

> maggie and milly and molly and may
>
> went down to the beach (to play one day)

a How would you describe the mood in this first stanza? How does the stanza make **you** feel? Note ✏ down **one** or **two** words to describe the mood as precisely as you can. You could choose from the ideas above, or use your own.

....

b Which words in the first stanza help to create the mood you have identified? Circle Ⓐ **one** or **two** of them.

(2) Now look at another two stanzas from the poem.

> and molly was chased by a horrible thing
>
> which raced sideways while blowing bubbles: and
>
> may came home with a smooth round stone
>
> as small as a world and as large as alone.

The mood of a poem can change as it develops, sometimes creating a surprising mixture of moods.

a How would you describe the mood in these stanzas? How do they make **you** feel? Note ✏ down **one** or **two** words that describe the mood or moods created in these stanzas as precisely as you can. You could choose from the ideas above, or use your own.

....

b Which words in these stanzas help to create the mood or moods you have identified? Circle Ⓐ **two** or **three** of them and label ✏ them with the mood or feeling they create.

3 How do I know whether my personal response is the right response?

A poem may be 'about' more than it first appears to be. A poem may describe a small event – but it may be the poet's intention to prompt big ideas in the reader. **Any** response that is supported by evidence, and shows that you have understood and responded to **some** or **all** of the ideas in the poem, will **always** be right.

① Look at some of these responses to the poem *maggie and milly and molly and may* on page 10.

Response	✗	✓	Evidence
A The poem is about some children playing on a beach.	☐	☐	
B The poem explores how children respond differently to things they find at the seaside.	☐	☐	
C The poem is about how all children are individuals.	☐	☐	
D The poem explores the idea that childhood can be a difficult time in our lives.	☐	☐	
E The poem is about the ways in which the world can be both comforting and frightening.	☐	☐	

a For each response, note 🖉 down a short quotation from the poem to support it. If you cannot find any relevant evidence, put a cross ✗ in the first check box next to the response instead.

b Which of the responses are most and least developed? Label 🖉 them '**most**' and '**least**'.

c Which **one** of these responses do you agree with most strongly? Put a tick ✓ in the second check box alongside your chosen response.

② When you have developed your response to the parts of the poem you feel more confident about, you can try to develop a response to some of the more challenging parts of the poem.

For whatever we lose (like a you or a me) ———— How can we lose 'a you or a me'?

it's always ourselves we find in the sea ———— How can we 'find ourselves' in the sea?

a What might the poet be suggesting in the **final** stanza? Note 🖉 down some possible ideas.

.... ☐

.... ☐

.... ☐

b Which of your ideas do you agree with most strongly? Tick ✓ them.

Developing a personal response

To develop a personal response to a poem, you need to:

- think about the ideas and images in the poem and try to find some connection between them
- identify the mood or moods created in the poem and consider how, and why, they change
- think about the bigger ideas the poet might be exploring in the poem
- most importantly, check you can support your response with evidence from the poem.

Now look at this exam-style question you saw at the start of the unit.

Exam-style question

Compare the ways the writers present childhood in *maggie and milly and molly and may* and *Legend*.

Look at these paragraphs taken from two students' responses to the question, focusing on *maggie and milly and molly and may*.

Student A

Childhood is presented as a time when we play and have fun. For example, Maggie finds a shell 'that sang' and Milly 'befriended' a starfish. These images create a positive mood and suggest that the seaside is a place where children can forget their 'troubles' and get closer to nature.

However, childhood can also be a time of fear: Molly was 'chased by a horrible thing'. The poet does not say what this 'thing' was, but describing it as a 'thing' suggests what a strange and terrifying creature it was and how terrified a child might have been.

Student B

At the start of the poem, the words 'beach' and 'play' suggest that the children have gone to the seaside for a fun day out, which is a typical thing to do in childhood, but this idea changes as the poem develops. Although some of the images in the poem are positive, most have a negative side. Maggie has 'troubles', Milly 'befriended' a starfish, which could suggest she is lonely, and Molly is chased by 'a horrible thing'. The impression this creates is that children are all individuals who cope in different ways with different problems, suggesting that childhood is a time when we 'find ourselves' because we find out what we are really like.

	Student A	Student B	Neither
1 a Which student has developed their response by finding ways to connect the different ideas in the poem? ✓	☐	☐	☐
b Which student has commented on the mood of the poem? ✓	☐	☐	☐
c Which student has explored some of the bigger ideas in the poem? ✓	☐	☐	☐

Your turn!

You are now going to **write two paragraphs** in response to the exam-style question.

Exam-style question

Compare the ways the writers present childhood in *maggie and milly* and *molly and may* and *Legend*.

In your answer you should compare:
- the ideas in the poems
- the poets' use of language
- the poets' use of form and structure.

Use evidence from the poems to support your **comparison**. (20 marks)

(1) Before you start to plan your response, consider the key point in the question: how is childhood presented in the poem? Think about:

? what happens at the beach   **?** how the children respond   **?** what this reveals about them

? the moods created in the poem   **?** bigger ideas the poet might be exploring

A

B

C

D

E

(a) How is childhood presented? Note ✎ down **five** key ideas in the poem in boxes A–E above.

(b) Add ✎ evidence to support each idea you have noted.

(c) What connections can you make between the ideas you noted? Draw ✎ lines linking any of the key ideas above that are connected. Annotate ✎ the lines to explain the connections.

(d) Review your ideas, evidence and connections. Tick ✓ those you will include in your writing.

(2) Now write ✎ **two** paragraphs on paper in response to the exam-style question, focusing on *maggie and milly* and *molly and may* **only**.

Review your skills

Check up

Review your response to the exam-style question on page 15. Tick ✓ the column to show how well you think you have done each of the following.

	Not quite ✓	Nearly there ✓	Got it! ✓
identified connections between key ideas in the poem	☐	☐	☐
explored the moods created in the poem	☐	☐	☐
explored the bigger ideas in the poem	☐	☐	☐

Need more practice?

Look again at the exam-style question you have been working on in this unit.

Exam-style question

Compare the ways the writers present childhood in *maggie and milly and molly and may* and *Legend*.

In your answer you should compare:
• the ideas in the poems
• the poets' use of language
• the poets' use of form and structure.

Use **evidence** from the poems to support your **comparison**.   (20 marks)

Now read *Legend* by Gillian Clarke, which can be found on page 74. When you have read it twice:
• think about the ideas and images in the poem and try to find some connection between them
• identify the mood or moods created in the poem and consider how, and why, they change
• think about the bigger ideas the poet might be exploring in the poem
• most importantly, check you can support your response with evidence from the poem.

Write ✎ **one** paragraph in response to the exam-style question, focusing your response on *Legend* by Gillian Clarke **only**. You'll find some suggested points to refer to in the Answers section.

Comparison practice

Write ✎ **one** or **two** paragraphs in response to the exam-style question, **comparing** your response to *maggie and millie and molly and may* with your response to *Legend*. You'll find some suggested points to refer to in the Answers section.

How confident do you feel about each of these **skills?** Colour ✎ in the bars.

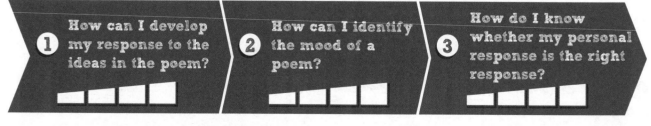

1 How can I develop my response to the ideas in the poem?

2 How can I identify the mood of a poem?

3 How do I know whether my personal response is the right response?

③ Exploring structure

This unit will help you to explore the poet's use of structure in an unseen poem. The skills you will build are to:

- track the structure and development of ideas in a poem
- analyse the impact of structural features in a poem
- comment effectively on structure.

In the exam you will face a question like the one below. At the end of the unit you will **write two paragraphs** in response to this question, focusing on **one of these poems**: *Otherwise*, on the next page. You will then have an opportunity to explore the second poem and compare them both.

Exam-style question

Compare the ways the writers present their lives in *Otherwise* and *Mother to Son*.

In your answer you should compare:
- the ideas in the poems
- the poets' use of language
- the poets' use of form and structure.

Use **evidence** from the poems to support your **comparison**.   (20 marks)

Before you tackle the question you will work through three key questions in the **skills boosts** to help you explore the poem's structure.

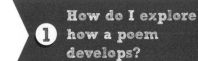
① How do I explore how a poem develops?

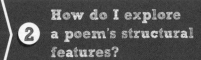
② How do I explore a poem's structural features?

③ How do I comment on structure?

Read the poem on the next page. In Paper 2, Section B, Part 2 of your English Literature exam, you will compare **two** unseen poems.

As you read the poem, think about: ⊘

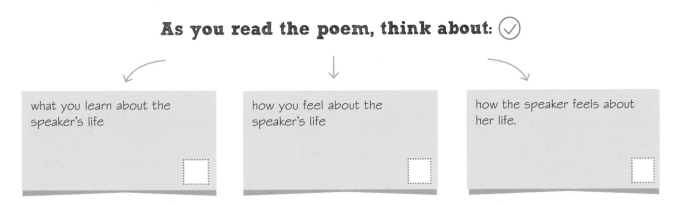

what you learn about the speaker's life

how you feel about the speaker's life

how the speaker feels about her life.

Otherwise

I got out of bed
on two strong legs.
It might have been
otherwise. I ate
5   cereal, sweet
milk, ripe, flawless
peach. It might
have been otherwise.
I took the dog uphill
10   to the birch wood.
All morning I did
the work I love.

At noon I lay down
with my mate. It might
15   have been otherwise.
We ate dinner together
at a table with silver
candlesticks. It might
have been otherwise.
20   I slept in a bed
in a room with paintings
on the walls, and
planned another day
just like this day.
25   But one day, I know,
it will be otherwise.

Jane Kenyon

① What do you think the speaker in this poem will do tomorrow? Write 🖉 a list below.

....

....

....

....

....

....

....

....

....

....

1 How do I explore how a poem develops?

Tracking the ideas or events described in a poem will help you explore the ways in which it develops.

① Some of the methods a poet may use to give a poem structure include:

Time	The poem tracks an idea or experience over a period of seconds, minutes, hours, days, or years.	*For example, a poem might compare the past and the present, or describe the present and imagine the future.*	☐
Movement	The poem moves through a setting, observing and recording it.	*For example, a poem might describe a busy city, or a beautiful landscape.*	☐
Narrative	The poem tells a story in a series of scenes or images.	*For example, a poem might show some key moments in a relationship.*	☐

a How is the poem *Otherwise* on page 18 structured? Tick ✓ one of the structural methods above.

b On page 18, underline Ⓐ **all** the key words or phrases in the poem that create this structure.

c Write ✐ **one** or **two** sentences explaining in more detail how the poem is structured.

....

....

....

② The final lines of a poem are often the most significant: they reflect on and develop the ideas explored in the poem. Final lines can typically serve the following purposes:

A conclusion	Looking in a new light	A sudden reversal
The final lines connect, and reflect on, all the ideas in the poem.	The final lines look again at the key ideas in the poem in a very different way, leading the reader to think again about all that they have just read.	The final lines reflect on the key ideas in the poem and come to an unexpected or shocking realisation.

For example, having reflected on the things she does in her life, the writer of the poem 'Otherwise' could have:

concluded what a happy, peaceful life she has.	*revealed that her 'mate' has a very different view of their life together.*	*decided that happiness and peace are repetitive and boring – she wants excitement and change.*

a Which lines in the poem *Otherwise* would you describe as its 'final lines'? Highlight ✐ them.

b How would you describe the final lines of the poem? Are they a **conclusion**, a **sudden reversal**, **looking in a new light**, or something else? Write ✐ **one** or **two** sentences explaining your ideas.

....

....

....

2 How do I explore a poem's structural features?

Exploring key structural features, such as viewpoint, timeframe, repetition and contrast, can reveal some of the principal ways in which the poet presents ideas.

pronouns: used in place of a noun, e.g. 'I', 'you', 'he', 'she', 'it', 'we', 'they'

tense: a verb form indicating **when** an action took place, e.g. past tense, present tense

repetition: a word or phrase repeated for effect

contrast: two very different objects or ideas closely positioned to highlight their differences

1. Looking at the poet's use of pronouns can reveal how the poet has used different **viewpoints** to structure the poem. Look at the poet's use of pronouns in *Otherwise* on page 18. What does it reveal about the poem? Tick ✓ the viewpoint the writer has mainly used.

I	The poem is mainly focused on the thoughts and feelings of the speaker.	☐
you we	The poem focuses on the speaker's relationship with one or more other people.	☐
he she they	The poem is a reflection on characters whose actions, thoughts, etc. are described in the poem.	☐

2. Looking at the poet's use of tense (e.g. the past tense, present tense, etc.) can reveal how the poet has structured the **timeframe** of the poem. In *Otherwise*, the poet writes about:

   • the actual past: ....

   • a possible past: ....

   • a definite future: ....

   Add ✐ a quotation alongside each point to show where the poet has used these tenses.

3. **Repetition** can be used in a poem to highlight or emphasise a key idea.

   a. Identify a word or phrase that is repeated in *Otherwise* on page 18. Circle Ⓐ it every time it appears in the poem.

   b. What idea is the poet emphasising through her repetition of this word or phrase? Write ✐ **one** or **two** sentences explaining your ideas.

   ....

   ....

   ....

4. **Contrast** can be used in a poem to highlight a significant difference or change in two very different people, places or situations.

   a. Identify an example of contrast in *Otherwise* on page 18. Write ✐ '**Contrast**' in the middle of the space to the right of the poem and draw ✐ linking lines to all the ideas in the poem that highlight this contrast.

   b. What idea does this contrast highlight? Write ✐ **one** or **two** sentences explaining your ideas.

   Look again at your answers to questions 2 and 3.

   ....

   ....

   ....

How do I comment on structure?

Comments on the **effect** of the poet's use of **structure** can be used to develop your ideas, and help you to explore the poet's **intention**.

(1) Look at two **key ideas** from the poem that a student identified in her response to a question about how the writer presents her life in the poem *Otherwise*.

> The speaker reflects on her happiness, and her good fortune in having that happiness. ☐

> The speaker realises that her life will change. ☐

Which **one** of these key ideas do you agree with most strongly? Tick ✓ it.

(2) Now look at some of the **evidence** that the student selected to support their ideas.

> 'It might / have been otherwise.' ☐

> 'But one day, I know, / it will be otherwise.' ☐

> The poet describes her day from when 'I got out of bed' until 'I slept in a bed'. ☐

Which evidence would you use to support the key idea you chose in question (1)? Tick ✓ it.

(3) Look at some **structural features** that the student focused on in exploring their ideas.

> This sentence is repeated throughout the poem. ☐

> The speaker contrasts the present with the future. ☐

> The speaker uses the routine of her day to structure the poem. ☐

Which structural feature relates to your chosen key idea? Tick ✓ it.

(4) The student also identified the **effect** of these structural features.

> This highlights the elements of her life that bring her happiness. ☐

> It emphasises her happiness and sense of relief that things have turned out as well as they have. ☐

> This creates a strong sense of her fear that things must and will change. ☐

Which of these effects would you link to the structural feature you chose in question (3)?
Tick ✓ it.

(5) The student reflected on what these structural features suggest about the poet's **intention**.

> This suggests that the poem is a reflection on the inevitable change that happens as we grow old. ☐

> This suggests that the poem is about the importance of knowing happiness cannot last. ☐

> This suggests that the poem is about the importance of appreciating your life as it is at the moment, not in the future. ☐

Which **one** of these is most relevant to all the other ideas you have selected? Tick ✓ it.

Exploring structure

To explore the poet's structural choices effectively, you need to:

- identify how the poet has structured the poem: for example, over a period of time, through movement, using narrative, etc.
- identify some of the poem's key structural features: for example, the use of pronouns, tense, repetition, contrast, etc.
- consider the effect of structure and structural features, and their contribution to the poet's intention.

Look at this exam-style question you saw at the start of the unit.

Exam-style question

Compare the ways the writers present their lives in *Otherwise* and *Mother to Son*.

In your answer you should compare:
- the ideas in the poems
- the poets' use of language
- the poets' use of form and structure.

Use **evidence** from the poems to support your **comparison**.   (20 marks)

Now look at a paragraph from one student's response to the question, focusing on *Otherwise*.

| identifies a key idea in the poem |
| supports key idea with evidence |
| identifies a structural element or feature |

The speaker gives a strong impression that she thinks she is very fortunate in her life. The poem is structured around the events of a typical day in her life, for example, it begins when she 'got out of bed' and then 'ate cereal' and it ends as she 'slept in a bed'. Each of these events highlights a positive aspect of her life: for example, she has 'two strong legs', suggesting she is healthy and she has 'silver candlesticks', suggesting she has wealth. After each of these events, she repeats the phrase 'It might have been otherwise'. The poem's structure and the use of repetition strongly imply how grateful she feels that everything she does and has in her life makes her happy and comfortable and that she can choose how she spends and enjoys her days.

| comments on the effect of the poet's structural choice |
| comments on how the effect of the structural choice supports the poet's intention |

(1) Can you identify all the different things the student has included in this paragraph? Draw ✐ lines to link the annotations to the paragraph to show where the student has included them.

Your turn!

You are now going to **write two paragraphs** in response to the exam-style question, focusing on *Otherwise* **only**.

> ### Exam-style question
>
> Compare the ways the writers present their lives in *Otherwise* and *Mother to Son*.
>
> In your answer you should compare:
> - the ideas in the poems
> - the poets' use of language
> - the poets' use of form and structure.
>
> Use **evidence** from the poems to support your **comparison**.
>
> (20 marks)

(1) Which of the **key ideas** in *Otherwise* will you focus on in your response? Note 🖉 them below.

Paragraph 1	Paragraph 2

(2) Now think about some of the poet's **structural choices**. Which are relevant to the key ideas you have noted? Add 🖉 them to your notes above.

(3) What **evidence** from the poem will you use to support your chosen key ideas and structural features? Add 🖉 quotations to your notes above.

(4) What comments will you make on the **effect** of the poet's use of structure? What comments will you make on its **contribution to the poet's intention**? Add 🖉 your ideas to your notes above.

(5) Review your notes. Tick ✓ the skills below you are ready to implement in the two paragraphs you are going to write.

- [ ] identify a key idea in the poem
- [ ] identify a structural feature that contributes to that key idea
- [ ] support your ideas with evidence from the poem
- [ ] explore the effect of the structural feature and its contribution to the poet's intention

(6) Now write 🖉 two paragraphs on paper in response to the exam-style question above, exploring the poet's use of structure in *Otherwise* **only**.

Review your skills

Check up

Review your response to the exam-style question on page 23. Tick ✓ the column to show how well you think you have done each of the following.

	Not quite ✓	Nearly there ✓	Got it! ✓
identified significant structural features	☐	☐	☐
explored the effect of structural features	☐	☐	☐
explored the contribution of structural features to the poet's intention	☐	☐	☐

Need more practice?

Look again at the exam-style question you have been working on in this unit.

Exam-style question

Compare the ways the writers present their lives in *Otherwise* and *Mother to Son*.

In your answer you should compare:
- the ideas in the poems
- the poets' use of language
- the poets' use of form and structure.

Use **evidence** from the poems to support your **comparison**.

(20 marks)

Now read *Mother to Son* by Langston Hughes on page 75. When you have read it twice:
- identify how the poet has structured the poem
- identify some of the poem's key structural features
- consider the effect of the structure and structural features, and their contribution to the poet's intention.

Write 🖉 **one** paragraph in response to the exam-style question, focusing on the poet's use of structure in *Mother to Son* by Langston Hughes **only**. You'll find some suggested points to refer to in the Answers section.

Comparison practice

Write 🖉 **one** or **two** paragraphs in response to the exam-style question, **comparing** the poet's use of structure in *Otherwise* **and** *Mother to Son*. You'll find some suggested points to refer to in the Answers section.

How confident do you feel about each of these **skills?** Colour 🖉 in the bars.

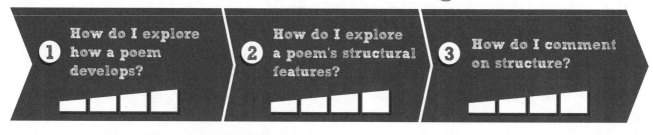

1 How do I explore how a poem develops?

2 How do I explore a poem's structural features?

3 How do I comment on structure?

Get started

Analyse the language, form and structure used by a writer to create meanings and effects (AO2)

④ Exploring the poet's language choices

This unit will help you to explore the poet's language choices in an unseen poem. The skills you will build are to:

- identify significant language choices
- explore the effect of significant language choices
- comment on the poet's language choices.

In the exam you will face a question like the one below. At the end of the unit you will **write two paragraphs** in response to this question, focusing on **one of these poems**: *City Lilacs*, on the next page. You will then have an opportunity to explore the second poem and compare them both.

Exam-style question

Compare the ways the writers present nature in *City Lilacs* and *A Letter in October*.

In your answer you should compare:
- the ideas in the poems
- the poets' use of language
- the poets' use of form and structure.

Use **evidence** from the poems to support your **comparison**. (20 marks)

Before you tackle the question you will work through three key questions in the **skills boosts** to help you explore the poet's language choices.

① How do I identify language choices that create a specific effect?

② How do I know what effect the poet is trying to create?

③ How do I comment on the poet's language choices?

Read the poem on the next page. In Paper 2, Section B, Part 2 of your English Literature exam, you will compare **two** unseen poems.

As you read the poem, think about:

the impressions the poet creates of the city

the impressions the poet creates of the people who live and work in cities

the impressions the poet creates of lilacs.

City Lilacs

In crack-haunted alleys, overhangs,
plots of sour earth that pass for gardens,
in the space between wall and wheelie bin,

where men with mobiles make urgent conversation,
5   where bare-legged girls shiver in April winds,
where a new mother stands on her doorstep and blinks
at the brightness of morning, so suddenly born —

in all these places the city lilacs are pushing
their cones of blossom into the spring
10   to be taken by the warm wind.

Lilac, like love, makes no distinction.
It will open for anyone.
Even before love knows that it is love
lilac knows it must blossom.

15   In crack-haunted alleys, in overhangs,
in somebody's front garden
abandoned to crisp packets and cans,

on landscaped motorway roundabouts,
in the depth of parks
20   where men and women are lost in transactions
of flesh and cash, where mobiles ring

and the deal is done — here the city lilacs
release their sweet, wild perfume
then bow down, heavy with rain.

Helen Dunmore

1 Write down **one** or **two** words or phrases to describe your impressions of the **three** different things the poet focuses on in the poem. As you note your ideas, label the line or phrase in the poem that creates each impression: **1a**, **1b**, etc.

The impression that the poet creates of…

1 the city	a ....
	b ....
2 people who live in the city	a ....
	b ....
3 the lilacs that grow in the city	a ....
	b ....

1 How do I identify language choices that create a specific effect?

When you read and write about a poem, aim to identify **rich, significant language choices** that the poet has chosen to create a specific effect on **you**, the reader.

To identify rich, significant language choices in the poem:

- focus on a small section of the poem at a time
- think about the poet's intention and your response to their ideas.

① Look at the **first** stanza of *City Lilacs*.

Complete the sentences below by ticking ✓ **one** word or phrase that most accurately describes your response.

> In crack-haunted alleys, overhangs,
>
> plots of sour earth that pass for gardens,
>
> in the space between wall and wheelie bin,

a In this stanza, the poet describes

the city ☐   the people in the city ☐   lilacs ☐

b The poet presents it/them as

beautiful ☐   clean ☐   tame ☐   strong ☐   busy ☐

united ☐   warm ☐   happy ☐   ugly ☐   dirty ☐   wild ☐

weak ☐   quiet ☐   isolated ☐   cold ☐   miserable ☐

② Now think about each word in the first stanza above. Which words create the impressions you identified in question ①?

a Cross out ~~cat~~ any words in the stanza that definitely do **not** create those impressions.

b Look at the words you have not crossed out. Which words create the impressions you have identified **most strongly**? Circle Ⓐ them.

③ Now look at the **second** stanza of the poem.

> where men with mobiles make urgent conversation,
>
> where bare-legged girls shiver in April winds,
>
> where a new mother stands on her doorstep and blinks
>
> at the brightness of morning, so suddenly born —

a What is the poet describing? ✐

....

b What impressions has the poet created of it/them? Note ✐ them below. You could use some of the ideas above, or use your own.

....

....

c Which words or phrases in the stanza create these impressions most strongly? Circle Ⓐ them.

2 How do I know what effect the poet is trying to create?

When you explore the effect of rich, significant language choices in a poem, or any text, think about the **connotations** of the word or phrase.

connotations: ideas or feelings that a word or phrase creates for the reader

(1) Look at this phrase in the **first** stanza of *City Lilacs* on page 26.

> In crack-haunted alleys, overhangs,
> plots of sour earth that pass for gardens,
> in the space between wall and wheelie bin,

Think about the connotations of the word 'sour' in this stanza.

Which ideas does it create in your mind?

Tick (✓) any of the ideas on the right, and/or add (✏) your own.

Mind map with central word **sour** *connected to:* nasty-tasting, unpleasant, bitter, spoilt, rotten, disgruntled, miserable

(2) The poet could have chosen different adjectives to describe the plots of earth in the city. What connotations would the following language choices have created? Note (✏) **two** ideas alongside each alternative word.

rich	....	....
sweet	....	....
plots of **sour** earth		
poor	....	....
starved	....	....

(3) Review your answers above. Write (✏) **one** or **two** sentences summing up your ideas about the poet's choice of the word 'sour' to describe the 'earth' in this city.

....

....

....

(4) Now look at these lines from the **second** stanza of *City Lilacs*.

> where men with mobiles make urgent conversation,
>
> where bare-legged girls shiver in April winds,

Circle (Ⓐ) **one** significant language choice in this stanza. Annotate (✏) it, identifying the connotations of your chosen word.

3 How do I comment on the poet's language choices?

The most effective comments on the poet's language choices focus on their **effect** on the reader and how they support the poet's **intention**.

intention: the impact the writer intends the text to have on the reader

① Look at this opening sentence of one student's analysis of *City Lilacs* on page 26.

> In the first line of the poem, the poet begins her description of the city with the image of 'crack-haunted alleys'.

This student could add one or more of the following comments to their sentence above.

A The poet is saying that the tarmac in the alleys is full of cracks. ☐

B This immediately gives the impression of a rundown and neglected city. ☐

C The word 'crack' could suggest neglect or it could suggest a drug problem haunts the city. ☐

D The word 'haunted' suggests this is an unwelcoming and frightening place. ☐

E This is a good description because you can imagine it in your mind. ☐

a Some of the comments above are **ineffective** because:
- they do not make a comment and are too vague. Label 🖉 them '**vague**' and cross ✕ them.
- they do not make a comment; they just describe what the writer has done. Label 🖉 them '**describe**' and cross ✕ them.

b Some of the comments above are **effective** because:
- they comment on the effect of a poetic device. Label 🖉 them '**effect**' and tick ✓ them.
- they comment on how the device supports the poet's intention. Label 🖉 them '**intention**' and tick ✓ them.

② The student's next paragraph begins: The poet then describes 'plots of sour earth'.

The student could add one or more of these comments. EITHER cross ✕ and label 🖉 them '**vague**' or '**describe**' OR tick ✓ and label 🖉 them '**effect**' or '**intention**'.

A The word 'sour' implies that the earth is rotten, perhaps suggesting pollution. ☐

B I think this is describing the gardens of the houses in the city. ☐

C The poet creates the impression of a ruined and polluted city where nothing will grow. ☐

D The word 'sour' makes me think this is not a good place. ☐

E This helps to convey the feeling of a place that no one cares about or looks after. ☐

Exploring the poet's language choices

To comment effectively on the poet's language choices, you need to:

- identify rich, significant language choices that contribute to the impressions created in the poem
- explore the connotations of the poet's language choices
- comment on their effect and their contribution to the poet's intention.

Now look at this exam-style question you saw at the start of the unit.

Exam-style question

Compare the ways the writers present nature in *City Lilacs* and *A Letter in October*.

In your answer you should compare:
- the ideas in the poems
- the poets' use of language
- the poets' use of form and structure.

Use **evidence** from the poems to support your **comparison**.

(20 marks)

Now look at a paragraph from one student's response to the question, focusing on *City Lilacs*.

identifies a key idea in the poem

comments on the connotations/ effect of language choice

> The poet then contrasts her description of a broken and neglected city with her description of the lilacs that grow there. She describes the lilacs 'pushing' their way into the city, which suggests their strength and power as though it takes a massive effort to squeeze into this crowded and unwelcoming place, and giving the impression of nature as powerful and something that will always survive. This strength of nature makes the city seem a better place, as though there is life and strength, not just loneliness and decay.

identifies a significant language choice

comments on how language choice supports the poet's intention

1. Can you identify all the different things the student has included in this paragraph? Draw ✏ lines to link the annotations to the paragraph to show where the student has included them.

Your turn!

You are now going to **write two paragraphs** in response to the exam-style question, focusing on *City Lilacs* only.

Exam-style question

Compare the ways the writers present nature in *City Lilacs* and *A Letter in October*.

In your answer you should compare:
- the ideas in the poems
- the poets' use of language
- the poets' use of form and structure.

Use **evidence** from the poems to support your **comparison**.   (20 marks)

---

(1) Choose **two** sections of the poem to focus on in your response. Choose sections which create a strong impression of nature. Label 🖉 them **1** and **2**.

(2) Look at the two sections of the poem you have selected. Circle (A) any rich, significant vocabulary choices in these sections that help to create a strong impression of nature.

(3) In the planning space below, note 🖉 down the impressions created in the two sections of the poem you have selected.

1	2

(4) Add 🖉 relevant quotations featuring significant vocabulary choices to your notes above.

(5) Annotate 🖉 significant vocabulary choices in each of your quotations with ideas about their connotations: what ideas and feelings do the poet's language choices create?

(6) Write 🖉 **two** paragraphs on paper in response to the exam-style question above, focusing on the poet's language choices.

Review your skills

Check up

Review your response to the exam-style question on page 31. Tick ✓ the column to show how well you think you have done each of the following.

	Not quite ✓	Nearly there ✓	Got it! ✓
identified significant language choices	☐	☐	☐
commented on their effect	☐	☐	☐
commented on their contribution to the poet's intention	☐	☐	☐

Need more practice?

Look again at the exam-style question you have been working on in this unit.

Exam-style question

Compare the ways the writers present nature in *City Lilacs* and *A Letter in October*.

In your answer you should compare:
- the ideas in the poems
- the poets' use of language
- the poets' use of form and structure.

Use **evidence** from the poems to support your **comparison**.   (20 marks)

Now read *A Letter in October* by Ted Kooser, which can be found on page 76. When you have read it twice:
- identify any rich, significant language choices that contribute to the impressions created in the poem
- consider the connotations of, and possible ambiguity in, the poet's language choices
- consider their effect and their contribution to the poet's intention.

Write ✏ **one** paragraph in response to the exam-style question, focusing on the poet's language choices in *A Letter in October* by Ted Kooser **only**. You'll find some suggested points to refer to in the Answers section.

Comparison practice

Write ✏ **one** or **two** paragraphs in response to the exam-style question, **comparing** the poets' language choices in *City Lilacs* **and** *A Letter in October*. You'll find some suggested points to refer to in the Answers section.

How confident do you feel about each of these **skills?** Colour ✏ in the bars.

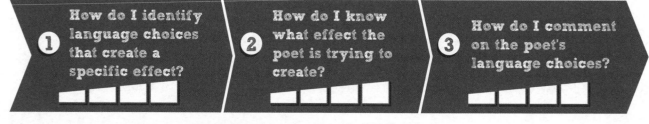

1 How do I identify language choices that create a specific effect?

2 How do I know what effect the poet is trying to create?

3 How do I comment on the poet's language choices?

⑤ Exploring poetic devices

This unit will help you to explore some of the language devices poets use to create meaning and effects. The skills you will build are to:

- identify and explore the impact of sound devices in a poem
- identify and explore the impact of imagery in a poem
- comment effectively on the poet's use of language devices.

In the exam you will face a question like the one below. At the end of the unit you will **write two paragraphs** in response to this question, focusing on **one of these poems**: *The Round*, on the next page. You will then have an opportunity to explore the second poem and compare them both.

Exam-style question

Compare the ways the writers present nature in *The Round* and *A Letter in October*.

In your answer you should compare:
- the ideas in the poems
- the poets' use of language
- the poets' use of form and structure.

Use **evidence** from the poems to support your **comparison**.   (20 marks)

Before you tackle the question you will work through three key questions in the **skills boosts** to help you explore the poet's use of poetic devices.

 1 How do I explore sound devices in a poem?   **2** How do I explore the imagery in a poem?   **3** How do I comment on the poet's use of poetic devices?

Read the poem on the next page. In Paper 2, Section B, Part 2 of your English Literature exam, you will compare **two** unseen poems.

As you read the poem, think about: ✓

| where the speaker is in the first part of the poem | why the speaker goes inside in the second part of the poem | the thoughts and feelings the poet expresses in the final part of the poem. |

The Round ✏

Light splashed this morning
on the shell-pink **anemones**
swaying on their tall stems;
down blue-spiked **veronica**
5   light flowed in rivulets
over the humps of the honeybees;
this morning I saw light kiss
the silk of the roses
in their second flowering,
10   my late bloomers
flushed with their brandy.
A curious gladness shook me.

So I have shut the doors of my house,
so I have trudged downstairs to my cell,
15   so I am sitting in semi-dark
hunched over my desk
with nothing for a view
to tempt me
but a bloated compost heap,
20   steamy old stinkpile,
under my window;
and I pick my notebook up
and I start to read aloud
the still-wet words I scribbled
25   on the blotted page:
"Light splashed . . ."

I can scarcely wait till tomorrow
when a new life begins for me,
as it does each day,
30   as it does each day.

Stanley Kunitz

anemones, veronica: flowering plants often found in a garden

1 a The title of this poem, *The Round*, could have a number of different meanings. Which of these meanings might the poet have intended? Tick ✓ **one** or **more**.

round (noun)

a a circular slice of something: *two rounds of toast.* ☐

b visits made to a number of people or places in turn:
I have a newspaper round, delivering papers in my local area. ☐

c one of a series of sessions or stages: *United are in the third round of the Cup.* ☐

d a regularly repeated sequence of activities:
My life is a daily round of school, homework and sleep. ☐

b What evidence in the poem points towards the definition you chose?

How do I explore sound devices in a poem?

Sound devices are language techniques that use the sound of a word or phrase to add to its impact.

onomatopoeia	a word whose sound imitates its meaning	bang crash
alliteration	words beginning with, or containing, the same letter or sound, positioned close to each other	feelings of love linger
assonance	words with similar vowel sounds, placed close to each other	bad habits can travel

(1) Circle (A) and label (✎) examples of 'onomatopoeia', 'alliteration', or 'assonance' in the extracts below from *The Round* on page 34.

> A   Light splashed this morning
>
> on the shell-pink anemones
>
> swaying on their tall stems;

> B   light flowed in rivulets
>
> over the humps of the honeybees;

(2) Read aloud any words you labelled 'onomatopoeia'. Why do you think the writer chose to use this device? Tick (✓) one or more of the ideas below, or add (✎) your own.

| It sounds good. | | It adds emphasis to the idea. | | |

| It makes the description more vivid. | | You can hear and see what the poet is describing. | |

(3) (a) Look at the words you labelled 'alliteration' in question (1). Highlight (✎) the alliterative letters. Read the lines aloud, emphasising the sound of the highlighted letters. Ask yourself:

- are they letters with **hard sounds** (e.g. 'k', 'p') or **soft sounds** (e.g. 's', 'w')?
- how does the sound of the letters contribute to the mood or impression of the poem?

(b) Complete (✎) one student's comments on the effect of this alliteration in the lines in question, using the ideas below.

> The hard alliterative sounds in these lines create a .... mood
>
> ....
>
> The soft alliterative sounds in these lines create a .... mood
>
> ....

| peaceful, quiet | suggesting the sound of | machinery | splashing water |
| violent, aggressive | creating an impression of | a gentle breeze | breaking glass |

(4) Assonance and alliteration can both create a strong link between words. Look at any phrases you labelled 'assonance' or 'alliteration' in question (1). Tick (✓) one or more of the ideas below to show their effect, or add (✎) your own.

| It sounds good. | | It adds emphasis to the idea. | | |

| It links two words to highlight a surprising image. | | It makes the description more vivid. | |

Skills boost

② How do I explore the imagery in a poem?

Imagery is the use of words to create visual images in the reader's mind. Writers often achieve this using **figurative language** techniques: simile, metaphor and personification.

simile	a comparison made using 'like' or 'as'
metaphor	a direct comparison
personification	a kind of metaphor that gives human actions or qualities to non-human objects

Similes are easy to identify:

- look for 'like' or 'as'
- is the writer comparing two things?

Metaphors are harder to spot:

- look for unusual or surprising word choices
- is the writer effectively comparing two things?

For example:

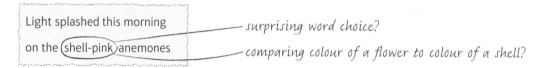

Light splashed this morning — *surprising word choice?*
on the (shell-pink) anemones — *comparing colour of a flower to colour of a shell?*

(1) In the lines above from *The Round* on page 34, has the writer used any other similes or metaphors? Circle Ⓐ and label 🖉 them.

(2) Look at this metaphor from the poem.

down blue-spiked veronica — *compares movement of light to movement of water*
(light flowed) in rivulets

Why do you think the poet has chosen to compare light and water in this metaphor? Think about the **qualities** and **connotations** of water.

| clean | pure | life-giving | refreshing | wet | fluid | sparkle | soak | pour |

Write 🖉 **one** or **two** sentences explaining your ideas. You could use some of the ideas above.

....

....

....

(3) Personification can also be a tricky technique to spot; look for surprising verb choices describing actions that are usually done only by humans. Look at the extract on the right.

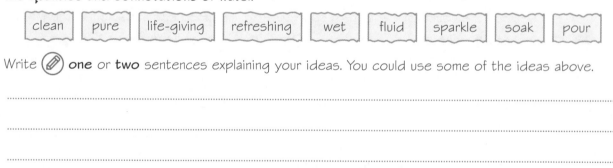

this morning I saw light (kiss)
the silk of the roses

a Annotate 🖉 the word 'kiss' with any qualities or connotations the word suggests to you.

b Why do you think the poet chose to describe the light landing on some roses as a 'kiss'? Write 🖉 **one** or **two** sentences explaining your ideas.

....

....

....

③ How do I comment on the poet's use of poetic devices?

The most effective comments on language and language devices focus on their **effect** on the reader and how they support the poet's **intention**.

① Look at these opening sentences of one student's analysis of *The Round* on page 34.

> *In the first part of the poem, the poet describes the beauty of his garden using surprising and vivid imagery. He describes seeing how the 'light splashed' on the flowers.*

This student could add one or more of the following comments to their sentences above.

A *This metaphor says that the light is like water.* ☐

B *This metaphor makes the movement of the light seem more dynamic and dramatic.* ☐

C *This metaphor makes the reader think.* ☐

D *This metaphor helps you imagine what it looked like more clearly.* ☐

E *This metaphor shows the poet's wonder and excitement at the beauty of the natural world.* ☐

a Some of the comments above are **ineffective** because:
- they do not make a comment and are too vague. Label 🖉 them '**vague**' and cross ⊗ them.
- they do not make a comment; they just describe what the writer has done. Label 🖉 them '**describe**' and cross ⊗ them.

b Some of the comments above are **effective** because:
- they comment on the effect of a poetic device. Label 🖉 them '**effect**' and tick ✓ them.
- they comment on how the device supports the poet's intention. Label 🖉 them '**intention**' and tick ✓ them.

② The student's next paragraph begins:
> *The poet uses alliteration in his description: 'splashed', 'swaying... stems'...*

The student could add one or more of these comments. EITHER cross ⊗ and label 🖉 them '**vague**' or '**describe**' OR tick ✓ and label 🖉 them '**effect**' or '**intention**'.

A *This alliteration uses lots of words beginning with 's'.* ☐

B *This alliteration sounds very effective and interesting.* ☐

C *This alliteration suggests the sound of a gentle breeze blowing through the flowers.* ☐

D *This alliteration creates a vivid impression of both the sight and sound of the poet's garden.* ☐

E *This alliteration suggests the calm, peaceful quiet of early morning.* ☐

Exploring poetic devices

To explore poetic devices effectively, you need to:

- identify any sound devices the poet has used
- identify any imagery the poet has used
- comment on their effect and their contribution to the poet's intention.

Look at this exam-style question you saw at the start of the unit.

Exam-style question

Compare the ways the writers present nature in *The Round* and *A Letter in October*.

In your answer you should compare:
- the ideas in the poems
- the poets' use of language
- the poets' use of form and structure.

Use **evidence** from the poems to support your **comparison**.   (20 marks)

Now look at a paragraph from one student's response to the question, focusing on *The Round*.

identifies a key idea in the poem

identifies a poetic device

In the second part of the poem, the speaker goes into his house to finish a poem about his experience in the garden. He uses the verb 'trudged' to suggest how reluctant he is to leave the beauty of the outside world, and describes the place he goes to write the poem in very negative terms. He uses the metaphor of a 'cell' to describe it, suggesting it is small and like being in prison. He describes his view of a compost heap as a 'steamy old stinkpile'. The alliteration of the letter 's' in this description almost suggests the hiss of the stinking fumes wafting up from the compost heap and floating in through his window. Both of these images use poetic devices to emphasise the difference between his experience inside the house, writing about the beauty of nature, compared with his experience outside the house, actually enjoying the beauty of nature.

comments on the effect of a poetic device

comments on how poetic devices support the poet's intention

① Can you identify all the different things the student has included in this paragraph? Draw lines to link the annotations to the paragraph to show where the student has included them.

Your turn!

You are now going to **write two paragraphs** in response to the exam-style question, focusing on the poet's use of **poetic devices**.

1 Look again at *The Round* on page 34. Tick ✓ **all** the poetic devices the poet uses.

Sound devices
alliteration
onomatopoeia
assonance

Imagery
simile
metaphor
personification

2 Look for key ideas where the poet uses a poetic device to add to their effect and impact.

a Note 🖉 down **two** key ideas in the poem that you will focus on in your response to the question.

b Add 🖉 quotations to your plan, labelling the poetic device the poet has used in each one.

3 What is the effect of the poetic devices in the quotations you have noted? Add 🖉 to your notes.

4 What is the poet's intention in the ideas and quotations you have noted? Add 🖉 to your notes.

5 Now write 🖉 **two** paragraphs on paper in response to the above exam-style question, focusing on the poet's use of poetic devices in *The Round*.

Remember: Don't simply list poetic devices that the poet uses. Only comment on poetic devices where they make a significant contribution to the poem's effect and the poet's intention.

Review your skills

Check up

Review your response to the exam-style question on page 39. Tick ✓ the column to show how well you think you have done each of the following.

	Not quite ✓	Nearly there ✓	Got it! ✓
explored the poet's use of sound devices	☐	☐	☐
explored the poet's use of imagery	☐	☐	☐
commented on poetic devices' effect and contribution to the poet's intention	☐	☐	☐

Need more practice?

Look again at the exam-style question you have been working on in this unit.

Exam-style question

Compare the ways the writers present nature in *The Round* and *A Letter in October*.

In your answer you should compare:
- the ideas in the poems
- the poets' use of language
- the poets' use of form and structure.

Use **evidence** from the poems to support your **comparison**.

(20 marks)

Now read *A Letter in October* by Ted Kooser, which can be found on page 76. When you have read it twice:
- identify any sound devices the poet has used
- identify any imagery the poet has used
- consider their effect and their contribution to the poet's intention.

Write ✐ **one** paragraph in response to the exam-style question, focusing on the poet's use of poetic devices in *A Letter in October* by Ted Kooser **only**. You'll find some suggested points to refer to in the Answers section.

Comparison practice

Write ✐ **one** or **two** paragraphs in response to the exam-style question, **comparing** the poet's use of poetic devices in *The Round* **and** *A Letter in October*. You'll find some suggested points to refer to in the Answers section.

How confident do you feel about each of these **skills?** Colour ✐ in the bars.

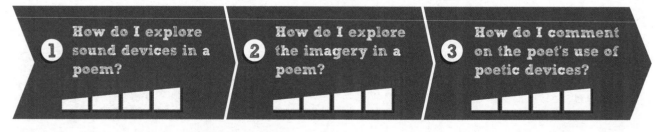

1. How do I explore sound devices in a poem?

2. How do I explore the imagery in a poem?

3. How do I comment on the poet's use of poetic devices?

⑥ Exploring the poet's use of form

This unit will help you to understand and explore how a poet uses form to create meaning and effects. The skills you will build are to:

* explore the form of a poem
* explore rhyme and rhythm in a poem
* comment effectively on the form of a poem.

In the exam you will face a question like the one below. At the end of the unit you will **write two paragraphs** in response to this question, focusing on **one of these poems**: *Postcard*, on the next page. You will then have an opportunity to explore the second poem and compare them both.

Exam-style question

Compare the ways the writers present nature in *Postcard* and *A Letter in October*.

In your answer you should compare:
* the ideas in the poems
* the poets' use of language
* the poets' use of form.

Use **evidence** from the poems to support your **comparison**.

(20 marks)

Before you tackle the question you will work through three key questions in the **skills boosts** to help you explore the form of a poem.

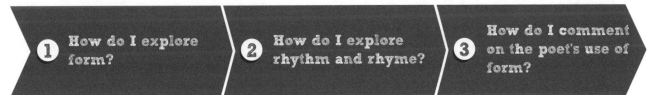

① **How do I explore form?**   ② **How do I explore rhythm and rhyme?**   ③ **How do I comment on the poet's use of form?**

Read the poem on the next page. In Paper 2, Section B, Part 2 of your English Literature exam, you will compare **two** unseen poems.

As you read the poem, think about: ✓

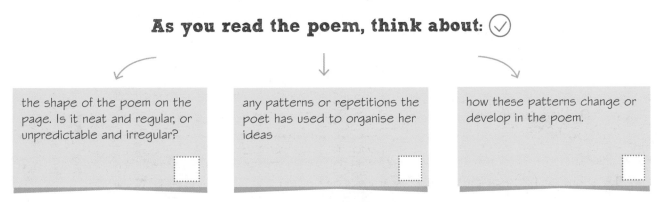

the shape of the poem on the page. Is it neat and regular, or unpredictable and irregular?

any patterns or repetitions the poet has used to organise her ideas

how these patterns change or develop in the poem.

Postcard

I saw a muskrat nose across a pond
nudging the reeds apart without a sound.

I saw a spider touched by a note of sun
shake out its net, bouncing it up and down.

5   I saw a black snake slipping off the road;
in the doorway, pulsing, a tiny golden toad.

I saw a white owl, baffled by the light
bank silently and sheer off out of sight.

These things took place the day the summer went.
10   I noted them down, not knowing what they meant

or if anything at all had really happened.
Only a state of mind in which eyes, opened

by solitude, could see the lives that other
creatures made, busy and unperturbed by love

15   or hate. I pull the shutters inward, drop the bar
but wind and dark still forage at my door.

Beatrice Garland

1 When did the poet write this poem, do you think?
Underline Ⓐ **two** clues you are given in the poem.

> How is the weather described
> at the end of the poem?

2 Which stanzas tell you most about the things the speaker sees? Label 🖉 them '**what she sees**'.

3 Which stanzas tell you most about the speaker's reaction to the things she sees? Label 🖉 them
'**reaction**'.

4 a How would you describe the form of this poem? Tick ✓ all the features below that you can
identify.

A | Lines are a regular length. | ☐

B | Lines are an irregular length. | ☐

C | Stanzas have the same number of lines. | ☐

D | Stanzas have a different number of lines. | ☐

E | Uses rhyme and half-rhyme. | ☐

F | Does not use any rhyme. | ☐

G | Uses repetition. | ☐

H | Does not use repetition. | ☐

b Highlight 🖉 examples of each feature in the poem and label them **A, B, C**, etc.

How do I explore form?

Before you can comment on form, you need to identify some of the features of form that the poet has used, then consider their effect.

One of the most immediately obvious features of a poem is the poet's choice of form. Look at the poem on the page and ask yourself: is the poem written in a **regular form**, with each stanza following a similar pattern? Or is it written in **free verse** with no obvious pattern?

Look at *Postcard* on page 42. The writer chose a **regular form** but she could have expressed the same ideas in **free verse**.

I saw a muskrat nose
across a pond nudging the reeds apart
without a sound.

I saw a spider

touched by a note
of sun shake out its net, bouncing it
up and
down.

I saw a muskrat nose across a pond
nudging the reeds apart without a sound.

I saw a spider touched by a note of sun
shake out its net, bouncing it up and down.

(1) Compare the two different versions of these stanzas. Which forms create which effects most powerfully? Complete the table below, ticking ✓ **regular form**, **free verse**, both or **neither**.

		Regular form ✓	Free verse ✓	Neither ✓
A	suggests a series of scenes or snapshots	☐	☐	☐
B	creates a gentle, reflective mood	☐	☐	☐
C	creates a mood of excitement or amazement	☐	☐	☐
D	imitates the informal patterns of everyday speech	☐	☐	☐
E	suggests a surprising sequence of random images	☐	☐	☐
F	highlights key words/phrases in each description	☐	☐	☐

(2) Now think about some of the other features of form you might find in a poem.
For example:
- repetition of words or phrases in the poem
- a sudden change in the form or pattern of stanzas.

(a) Can you identify either of these features in the poem on page 42? Highlight and label 🖉 them '**repetition**' or '**change in form/pattern**'.

(b) What effect do the features you identified have? On paper, write 🖉 **one** or **two** sentences describing the effects of the features you identified. You could use some of the ideas in question (1) to help you.

Unit 6 Exploring the poet's use of form   43

How do I explore rhythm and rhyme?

How do you talk when you are thinking aloud? How do you talk when you are angry, or happy, or miserable, or excited? Poets use rhythm to reflect those speech patterns and create the mood, pace and emphasis they want to achieve.

mood: the feeling or emotion created in a text
pace: the speed at which the ideas in a text develop or are expressed
emphasis: a specific word or phrase is highlighted or given more importance

Rhyme and rhythm work together to create **mood**, **pace** and **emphasis**.

① Compare the three versions of the **first** stanza of the poem *Postcard* below. Try reading them aloud to hear the impact of rhyme and rhythm.

1. The original version:

> I saw a muskrat nose across a pond
> nudging the reeds apart without a sound.

2. ...now without the rhyme:

> I saw a muskrat nose across a lake
> nudging the reeds apart without a noise.

3. ...now with a different rhythm:

> I saw a muskrat that was nosing silently across a lake nudging its way through the reeds

a What impact do the rhyme and rhythm of the original have? Complete the sentences below by circling Ⓐ any words to the right.

Remember: The changes may affect more than one aspect of the poem.

• Taking out the **rhyme** changes the:	mood	pace	emphasis
• Changing the **rhythm** changes the:	mood	pace	emphasis

b Write ✏ **one** or **two** sentences, describing the mood, pace, or emphasis created by rhyme and rhythm in the original version.

....

....

....

End-stopped lines can emphasise the rhythm of a poem. The use of **enjambment** can change the mood and/or pace of the poem and allow specific phrases to be emphasised.

end-stopped: when a line of poetry ends with a punctuation mark
enjambment: when a sentence runs on without pause from one line or stanza to the next

② Look closely at the last **four** stanzas of *Postcard* on page 42. Read them aloud. Cross out any unnecessary words in the sentences below so they accurately describe the effects of enjambment in these lines.

> The use of enjambment in the last four stanzas:
> • <u>maintains / changes</u> the **pace** of the poem, making it <u>faster / slower</u>.
> • <u>maintains / changes</u> the **mood** of the poem, making it <u>more / less</u> <u>anxious / excited / angry / reflective</u>.
> • gives **emphasis** to the <u>word / phrase</u> <u>'busy' / 'unperturbed by love' / 'or hate' / 'wind and dark'</u>.

How do I comment on the poet's use of form?

The most effective comments on the poet's use of form focus on the **effect** of the poet's choices on the reader and how they support the poet's **intention**.

> **intention:** the impact that the writer intends the text to have on the reader

① Re-read the poem *Postcard* on page 42. Draw ✎ lines to link some of the boxes below to summarise your comments on the form of the poem.

| In the first part of the poem | | In the second part of the poem | |

| the poet uses a regular stanza form | the poet uses a regular rhythm and rhyme | the poet uses free verse | the poet uses enjambment |

| to create a series of scenes or snapshots | to focus on different ideas or aspects of a scene or idea | to suggest disconnected or random thoughts | to suggest the patterns of everyday speech |

| to create a slower, measured pace | to create a regular, even pace | to create a faster pace |

| to create a reflective, thoughtful mood | to create a mood of excitement | to suggest that the speaker's thoughts are suddenly racing | to create an anxious, unsettled mood |

> Learn the spelling of **rhythm**. The first three letters are the same as 'rhyme' – and it has two 'h's, one 'y' and **no vowels**. Think: <u>r</u>hythm <u>h</u>elps <u>y</u>our <u>t</u>wo <u>h</u>ips <u>m</u>ove.

② Which of the features of form below would you expect to find in (and use if you were writing):

- an angry poem about the end of a relationship? Label ✎ them **A** for 'angry'.
- a poem exploring happy memories? Label ✎ them **M** for 'memories'.
- a poem about childhood? Label ✎ them **C** for 'childhood'.

| a regular stanza form ☐ | free verse ☐ |

| a regular rhythm ☐ | no regular rhythm ☐ | enjambment ☐ |

| short lines ☐ | longer lines ☐ |

| some rhyme and half rhyme ☐ | no rhyme ☐ |

| a slower pace ☐ | a regular, even pace ☐ | a faster pace ☐ |

Exploring the poet's use of form

To comment effectively on the poet's use of form, you need to:
- identify features of the poem's form that have a significant effect
- explore their effect on the reader and/or contribution to the poet's intention.

Now look again at the exam-style question you saw at the start of the unit.

Exam-style question

Compare the ways the writers present nature in *Postcard* and *A Letter in October*.

In your answer you should compare:
- the ideas in the poems
- the poets' use of language
- the poets' use of form.

Use **evidence** from the poems to support your **comparison**.   (20 marks)

Look at these paragraphs taken from students' responses to the question, focusing on *Postcard*.

Student A

The poem is written in stanzas of two lines. These are called couplets. The poet uses rhyme and half rhyme to link each pair of lines, for example, 'pond' and 'sound', and there is quite a regular rhythm which helps the poem flow. The poet also uses enjambment which means that some lines flow into the next one without stopping. This is quite effective.

Student B

In the second part of the poem the poet uses enjambment to hurry the pace of the poem, suggesting fast-moving thoughts as the speaker reflects on the idea that animals' lives are 'busy and unperturbed by love / or hate'. Finishing this sentence so quickly on the new line brings the hurried pace to a sudden halt, which emphasises the phrase 'or hate' and suggests that the speaker, unlike the animals, *is* feeling perturbed and is especially perturbed by hate.

Student C

The poet uses each one of the first four stanzas of the poem to show snapshots from the speaker's life on the last day of summer. Each stanza follows a similar pattern, using a similar rhythm, and repetition of the phrase 'I saw', to create an even, measured pace suggesting a calm mood of reflection. It creates the impression of a quiet walk through the countryside, observing wildlife as the summer comes to an end.

(1) (a) Which students have identified significant features of the poem's **form**?

....

(b) Which students have commented effectively on the **effect** of the poem's form or the poet's intention?

....

Your turn!

You are now going to **write two paragraphs** in response to the exam-style question, focusing on the poet's **use of form**.

Exam-style question

Compare the ways the writers present nature in *Postcard* and *A Letter in October*.

In your answer you should compare:
- the ideas in the poems
- the poets' use of language
- the poets' use of form.

Use **evidence** from the poems to support your **comparison**. (20 marks)

In your response, you could focus on some of these key ideas in the poem:

- the animals described ——————— I saw a spider touched by a note of sun

- feelings of love and hate ———————

  the lives that other
  creatures made, busy and unperturbed by love
  or hate. I pull the shutters inward, drop the bar

- the arrival of autumn ——————— but wind and dark still forage at my door.

(1) Use the planning space below to note ✎ **two** key ideas in *Postcard* on which you will focus in your response. You could use some of the ideas above, and/or your own ideas.

(2) How does the poet's use of form contribute to these ideas? Add ✎ quotations and notes to the planning space above.

(3) Review your notes. Have you focused on the **effect** of the poet's use of form? Adjust ✎ your notes as necessary.

(4) Write ✎ **two** paragraphs on paper in response to the exam-style question above, focusing on the poet's use of form in *Postcard* **only**.

Review your skills

Check up

Review your response to the exam-style question on page 47. Tick ✓ the column to show how well you think you have done each of the following.

	Not quite ✓	Nearly there ✓	Got it! ✓
identified significant features of form	☐	☐	☐
commented on their effect and/or contribution to the poet's intention	☐	☐	☐

Need more practice?

Look again at the exam-style question you have been working on in this unit.

Exam-style question

Compare the ways the writers present nature in *Postcard* and *A Letter in October*.

In your answer you should compare:
* the ideas in the poems
* the poets' use of language
* the poets' use of form.

Use **evidence** from the poems to support your **comparison**.

(20 marks)

Now read *A Letter in October* by Ted Kooser, which can be found on page 76. When you have read it twice:
* identify features of the poem's form that have a significant effect
* explore their effect on the reader and/or contribution to the poet's intention.

Write ✐ **one** paragraph in response to the exam-style question, focusing on the poet's use of form in *A Letter in October* by Ted Kooser **only**. You'll find some suggested points to refer to in the Answers section.

Comparison practice

Write ✐ **one** or **two** paragraphs in response to the exam-style question, **comparing** the poets' use of form in *Postcard* and *A Letter in October*. You'll find some suggested points to refer to in the Answers section.

How confident do you feel about each of these **skills**? Colour ✐ in the bars.

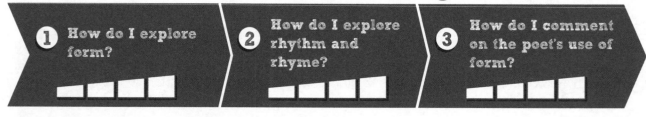

1 How do I explore form?

2 How do I explore rhythm and rhyme?

3 How do I comment on the poet's use of form?

Get started

Read, understand and respond to texts (AO1); Analyse the language, form and structure used by a writer to create meanings and effects (AO2)

⑦ Analysing a poem

This unit will help you to analyse a poem in preparation for comparing it with another. The skills you will build are to:

- annotate a poem
- explore how different elements of a poem work together to create effects
- select and sequence significant points to make in your response.

In the exam you will face a question like the one below. At the end of the unit you will identify the most significant ideas and elements in the poem on the next page and begin to **plan your response**. You will then have an opportunity to explore the second poem and compare them both.

> **Exam-style question**
>
> Compare the ways the writers present relationships in *Strawberries* and *When You Are Old*.
>
> In your answer you should compare:
> - the ideas in the poems
> - the poets' use of language
> - the poets' use of form.
>
> Use **evidence** from the poems to support your **comparison**. (20 marks)

Before you tackle the question you will work through three key questions in the **skills boosts** to help you plan your response and write effectively about the poem.

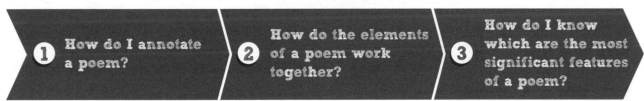

① How do I annotate a poem?

② How do the elements of a poem work together?

③ How do I know which are the most significant features of a poem?

Read the poem on the next page. In Paper 2, Section B, Part 2 of your English Literature exam, you will compare **two** unseen poems.

As you read the poem, think about: ⊘

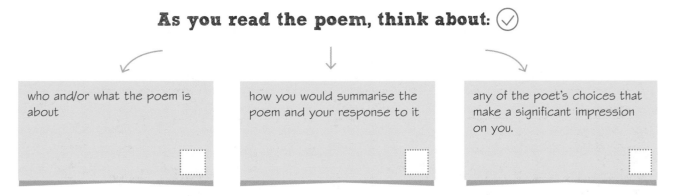

| who and/or what the poem is about | how you would summarise the poem and your response to it | any of the poet's choices that make a significant impression on you. |

Strawberries

There were never strawberries
like the ones we had
that sultry afternoon
sitting on the step
5 of the open french window
facing each other
your knees held in mine
the blue plates in our laps
the strawberries glistening
10 in the hot sunlight
we dipped them in sugar
looking at each other
not hurrying the feast
for one to come
15 the empty plates
laid on the stone together
with the two forks crossed
and I bent towards you
sweet in that air
20 in my arms
abandoned like a child
from your eager mouth
the taste of strawberries
in my memory
25 lean back again
let me love you

let the sun beat
on our forgetfulness
one hour of all
30 the heat intense
and summer lightning
on the **Kilpatrick hills**

let the storm wash the plates

Edwin Morgan

Kilpatrick hills: an area in Scotland

1 Which word, phrase or line in the poem do you find particularly effective? Underline Ⓐ it, then write 🖉 **one** or **two** sentences explaining your choice.

....
....
....
....
....
....

1   How do I annotate a poem?

Don't start with a checklist of features to spot in the poem – similes, metaphors, rhyme, enjambment, etc. Start with the poem and your response to the ideas you find in it. You can then think about how the poet's choices have shaped those ideas and your response.

(1) When you first read a poem, aim only to understand what it is about. Then read it again to make sure you feel confident in your understanding. Write ✏ **one** short sentence summarising the poem *Strawberries* on page 50.

....

....

(2) Read the poem a third time. Identify any words, phrases or ideas that seem significant in shaping your understanding. For example:

a When did you first realise that the poem is about two lovers? Underline Ⓐ the word or phrase in the poem on page 50 that first suggested this idea to you.

b Annotate ✏ the rest of the poem, noting what happens, and your impressions of the people, or events, keeping your notes on the **left-hand side of the poem.** Save the space on the right-hand side for annotating some of the poet's choices.

> For more on understanding and responding to a poem, see Units 1 and 2.

(3) Are there any words, phrases, ideas or images that surprised or mystified you in this poem? Circle Ⓐ them. Think about why the poet might have used them. These are the parts of the poem that might create the most effective and interesting response. For example:

a Why might the poet have chosen strawberries as the food the lovers eat in the poem? Why not an apple, or cake, or crisps? Annotate ✏ the title of the poem with your ideas.

b Look at lines 15–17 of the poem. Why might the poet have chosen to use this image?

> the empty plates
> laid on the stone together
> with the two forks crossed

Annotate these lines in the poem with your ideas, making notes on the **right-hand side of the poem.** ✏

c Now annotate ✏ any other words or phrases that seem significant in creating the ideas and impressions you have already noted on the poem. Think about what they suggest, their connotations, and how they shape your ideas and impressions.

> For more on language and poetic devices, see Units 4 and 5.

(4) You can now begin to think about the poet's choices of form and structure. For example:

a The poem is written in very short lines. What effect does this have on your impressions, and the mood or pace of the poem? Note ✏ your ideas on the **right-hand side of the poem.**

b The final line of the poem is given its own stanza. What effect does this have? Annotate ✏ the final line with your ideas, noting them on the **right-hand side of the poem.**

c Can you identify any other significant features of form and/or structure? How do they contribute to the mood or pace of the poem? Annotate ✏ the poem with your ideas, noting them on the **right-hand side of the poem.**

> For more on structure and form, see Units 3 and 6.

2 How do the elements of a poem work together?

Aim to fully explore each piece of evidence you select, thinking about how different choices of language and/or form and structure work together.

(1) Think about all the different language choices in a quotation. Look at one student's annotations below of **two different language choices** in lines 20–21 of *Strawberries* on page 50. The speaker describes his lover being:

> two meanings:
> 1. uninhibited, carefree, unrestrained
> 2. deserted, left alone

in my arms
abandoned like a child

— helpless, innocent, vulnerable?

> together these suggest lover's been deserted, left
> in his arms, like a helpless child?
> Or that lover is carefree and innocent like a child?
> Or both?

Write ✏️ **one** or **two** sentences, commenting on the poet's language choices in these lines. You could use the notes above to help you, or your own ideas.

....

....

....

....

(2) Think about how language and structure work together in a quotation. Look at one student's annotations below of **a language choice and a structure choice** in lines 27–28 of the poem.

— short, simple language choices

let the sun beat
on our forgetfulness

— suggests strength, violence?

— last word on short line – adds emphasis

Write ✏️ **one** or **two** sentences commenting on the poet's choices of language and structure in these lines. You could use the notes above to help you, or your own ideas.

....

....

....

....

....

③ How do I know which are the most significant features of a poem?

The most significant features of a poem are those that make a significant contribution to the poem's key themes and the poet's intention.

① Look at some ideas about the poem *Strawberries* that one student has noted in response to the exam-style question on page 49.

Exam-style question

Compare the ways the writers present relationships in *Strawberries* and *When You Are Old*.

A strawberries – red, heart-shaped – suggest love ☐

B heat of summer described: 'sultry afternoon' – passion? ☐

C 'feast' contrasts with simple plate of strawberries – suggests simple pleasures transformed by love ☐

D image of forks crossed – reflects the closeness of the couple ☐

E 'heat intense / and summer lightning' – suggests heat has built to dramatic passion ☐

F final line – form and word choice emphasise focus on love, not cleaning up after feast ☐

ⓐ Which of the following are **key themes** in the poem that this student has focused on in their notes? Tick ✓ them.

| strawberries ☐ | weather ☐ | cleaning up ☐ |
| cutlery and crockery ☐ | | love and passion ☐ |

> Which themes link two or more of the student's points? Which themes does the poet want the reader to focus on?

ⓑ Look again at the key themes you have ticked. Label ✎ each of the student's ideas above with the relevant key theme.

② Now think about the poet's **intention**: the impact that the poet wanted these key themes to have on the reader.

ⓐ Which of the ideas below do you think describes the poet's intention most accurately? Tick ✓ one.

A The poet wants to describe the weather during a very hot summer that he remembers. ☐

B The poet wants to express the love and passion he feels in this relationship. ☐

C The poet likes strawberries and wants to express how important they are in his life. ☐

D The poet wants to express his view that love and relationships are much more important than housework. ☐

ⓑ Which of the student's ideas in question ① make the most significant contribution to the intention you have selected? Tick ✓ the **three** most significant.

Analysing a poem

To begin planning an effective response to the exam question you need to:
- annotate the poem, thinking about how the poet's choices have shaped your understanding and response to it
- explore how the poet's choices work together in the quotations you select
- identify the most significant features of each poem.

Now look at this exam-style question, which you saw at the start of the unit.

Exam-style question

Compare the ways the writers present relationships in *Strawberries* and *When You Are Old*.

In your answer you should compare:
- the ideas in the poems
- the poets' use of language
- the poets' use of form.

Use **evidence** from the poems to support your **comparison**.   (20 marks)

Look at one student's annotations of the poem *Strawberries*, written in response to the exam-style question.

A   facing each other
    your knees held in mine ————— emphasises closeness of speaker and his lover   ☐

B   strawberries glistening ————— strawberries described like jewels   ☐
    in the hot sunlight ————— hot = passion

C   sweet in that air ————— thinks strawberries or his lover are sweet? Or both?   ☐

D   your eager mouth ————— suggests lover feels the same passion as the speaker   ☐

E   lean back again
    let me love you ————— command verbs/short lines emphasise strength of his feeling?   ☐

F   let the sun beat ————— suggests heat of the day and the heat of their passion
    blanks out everything else
    on our forgetfulness ————— suggests both speaker and his lover share that feeling   ☐

① Which points are relevant to the exam-style question: that is, which points focus on the speaker's thoughts and feelings? Tick ✓ them.

② Which of the points you have ticked are relevant to the key **themes** of the poem and the poet's **intention**? Highlight ✐ the relevant letters.

③ Which of the points you have ticked **and** highlighted would allow the student to make significant comments on the poet's choices of language, structure and form? Note ✐ the letters below.

....

Your turn!

You are now going to begin **planning your own answer** in response to the exam-style question, focusing on *Strawberries*.

Exam-style question

Compare the ways the writers present relationships in *Strawberries* and *When You Are Old*.

In your answer you should compare:
- the ideas in the poems
- the poets' use of language
- the poets' use of form.

Use **evidence** from the poems to support your **comparison**.   (20 marks)

(1) Review your annotations of the poem on page 50. Which of your ideas are relevant to the exam-style question? Note 🖉 them below.

....

....

....

....

....

....

....

....

....

....

(2) Which of the points you have noted are relevant to the key themes of the poem and the poet's intention? Tick ✓ them.

(3) Which of the points you have ticked will allow you to make significant comments on the poet's choices of language, structure and form? Tick ✓ them again.

Review your skills

Check up

Review your response to the exam-style question on page 55. Tick ✓ the column to show how well you think you have done each of the following.

	Not quite ✓	Nearly there ✓	Got it! ✓
identified points that are relevant to the exam-style question	☐	☐	☐
identified points that are relevant to the key themes of the poem and the poet's intention	☐	☐	☐
identified points that will allow significant comment on the poet's choices	☐	☐	☐

Need more practice?

Look again at the exam-style question you have been working on in this unit.

Exam-style question

Compare the ways the writers present relationships in *Strawberries* and *When You Are Old*.

In your answer you should compare:
- the ideas in the poems
- the poets' use of language
- the poets' use of form.

Use **evidence** from the poems to support your **comparison**.   (20 marks)

Now read *When You Are Old* by William Butler Yeats, which can be found on page 73. When you have read it twice:
- annotate the poem, thinking about how the poet's choices have shaped your understanding and response to it
- explore how the poet's choices work together in the quotations you select
- identify the most significant features of the poem that are relevant to the exam-style question.

You'll find some suggested points to refer to in the Answers section.

Comparison practice

Write ✏ **one** or **two** paragraphs in response to the exam-style question, **comparing** *Strawberries* **and** *When You Are Old*. You'll find some suggested points to refer to in the Answer section.

How confident do you feel about each of these **skills**? Colour ✏ in the bars.

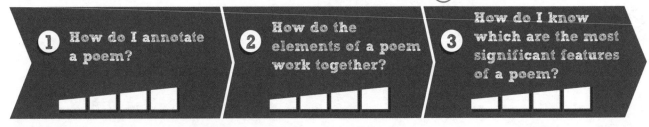

1 How do I annotate a poem?

2 How do the elements of a poem work together?

3 How do I know which are the most significant features of a poem?

Read, understand and respond to texts (AO1); Analyse the language, form and structure used by a writer to create meanings and effects (AO2)

⑧ Comparing poems

This unit will help you to compare the ways in which a similar theme or idea is presented in two poems. The skills you will build are to:

- identify relevant and significant similarities and differences in two poems
- develop a comparison of two poems
- structure a comparison of two poems.

In the exam you will face a question like the one below. This is about the poems on the next page. At the end of the unit you will **plan and write your response** to this question.

Exam-style question

Compare the ways the writers present someone's death in *My Grandfather's Garden* and *Poem*.

In your answer you should compare:
- the ideas in the poems
- the poets' use of language
- the poets' use of form.

Use **evidence** from the poems to support your **comparison**.

(20 marks)

Before you tackle the question you will work through three key questions in the **skills boosts** to help you compare two poems.

① How do I plan my comparison? **② How do I develop my comparison?** **③ How do I structure my comparison?**

Read both poems on the next page. In Paper 2, Section B, Part 2 of your English Literature exam, you will compare **two** unseen poems.

As you read each poem, think about: ✓

| what you learn about the speaker in the poem and the person who has died | the speaker's thoughts and feelings about the person who has died | the speaker's thoughts and feelings following the person's death. |

My Grandfather's Garden

Where bloodshot apples peered from the grass
and seed packets taught me the patience
of waiting through a season.

Where I cracked the seams of pods,
5   and fired out peas with a thumbnail
pushed along the down of the soft inside.

Where he kept order with hoe prods,
at the stems of lettuces, emerging like
overgrown moth-eaten flowers, colours drained.

10   Where I crouched on the shed's corrugate roof,
touching ripe damsons, which fell into the lap
of my stretched T-shirt.

Where I have come now, a month after his death,
the house and garden following him out of my life,
15   to cut back brambles and pack away tools.

Where, entering the hollow socket of the shed,
I hear damsons tap the roof,
telling me there is no one to catch them.

Owen Sheers

Poem

And if it snowed and snow covered the drive
he took a spade and tossed it to one side.
And always tucked his daughter up at night
And **slippered** her the one time that she lied.
5   And every week he tipped up half his wage.
And what he didn't spend each week he saved.
And praised his wife for every meal she made.
And once, for laughing, punched her in the face.

And for his mum he hired a private nurse.
10   And every Sunday taxied her to church.
And he blubbed when she went from bad to worse.
And twice he lifted ten quid from her purse.

Here's how they rated him when they looked back:
sometimes he did this, sometimes he did that.

Simon Armitage

slippered: to be physically punished by being beaten with a slipper

(1) a Which **one** line or image in each poem reveals most about the person who has died and/or the speaker's thoughts and feelings about them? Underline (A) it.

b For each poem, write 🖉 **one** or **two** sentences commenting on what is revealed or suggested in the lines or images you have underlined.

My Grandfather's Garden: ....

....

....

....

Poem: ....

....

....

....

How do I plan my comparison?

To begin planning your comparison, you need to think about the key ideas expressed in each poem.

① Begin by focusing on the key ideas in each poem, looking at them one at a time.

Ask yourself:

- Who and/or what is the poem about?
- How is this idea or subject presented?
- What is the speaker's viewpoint: are they focusing on themselves, or on someone else?
- What kinds of thoughts and feelings are expressed?

a Now summarise your ideas, comparing the two poems by completing these sentences. ✏

Both poems are about

....

....

However, My Grandfather's Garden focuses on

....

....

whereas in Poem the speaker describes

....

....

b Review the sentences you have written. Do they answer all the questions you asked yourself before you wrote them? If not, add ✏ to your sentences.

② Look at this list of key ideas and evidence from the two poems.

My Grandfather's Garden

> **a** seed packets taught me the patience of waiting through a season.

> **b** he kept order with hoe prods

> **c** the house and garden following him out of my life

Key ideas

> **A** Details of the life of the person who has died.

> **B** The speaker's thoughts and feelings about the person who has died.

> **C** The speaker's thoughts and feelings about their death.

Poem

> **d** And praised his wife for every meal she made. And once, for laughing, punched her in the face.

> **e** And he blubbed when she went from bad to worse. And twice he lifted ten quid from her purse.

> **f** Here's how they rated him when they looked back: sometimes he did this, sometimes he did that.

a Draw ✏ lines to link each key idea to relevant evidence from each poem.

b Compare each key idea in the two poems. Is it a similarity or a difference? For each key idea, circle Ⓐ either **S** for Similarity or **D** for difference.

Key idea A: S   D

Key idea B: S   D

Key idea C: S   D

2 How do I develop my comparison?

To develop your comparison of two poems you can:
- compare key ideas and how the poets present them in their choice of language, form and structure
- compare similar uses of language, form and structure in the poems and impacts that these have.

(1) Both poems create an impression of the person who has died. Compare these two pieces of evidence.

My Grandfather's Garden

> he kept order with hoe prods

Poem

> And praised his wife for every meal she made.
> And once, for laughing, punched her in the face.

a Identify **one** word or phrase in each quotation that creates the strongest impression of the person who has died. Circle (A) it.

b What impression does this word or phrase create? Complete (✏) the sentences below to explain your ideas, crossing out (~~out~~) one of the highlighted words as appropriate.

In My Grandfather's Garden, the speaker presents his grandfather as

....

....

Similarly/However, in Poem, the speaker creates the impression that the man who has died

....

(2) In addition to comparing the key ideas in the poems, you can compare the poets' choices of language, form and structure and the impact of those choices. Use some or all of the words and phrases below to compare (✏) as many of the poets' choices as you can.

For more help on language, form and structure, see Units 3–6.

In	both poems	My Grandfather's Garden	Poem
the poet uses	repetition	rhyme and end-stopped lines	enjambment
of	the word 'Where'	the word 'And'	
to emphasise	the different events in a life	the importance of this place	a key idea
to create	a slow pace	a fast pace	
and	a quiet, reflective mood	an abrupt, aggressive mood	
similarly	however	in the same way	whereas

....

....

....

....

....

3 How do I structure my comparison?

In each paragraph of your comparison, aim to compare the **key ideas** in the poem and how they are conveyed, exploring and comparing the **poets' choices** of language, form and structure.

① Look at the sentences below. They are from one paragraph of a student's response comparing *My Grandfather's Garden* and *Poem*.

Writing about both poems

A Both poems focus on the death of a person.

B *My Grandfather's Garden* focuses on the speaker's thoughts and feelings after his grandfather's death, whereas *Poem* focuses on everything a man did in his life and how people judged him.

C The poet uses enjambment throughout *My Grandfather's Garden* whereas each line of *Poem* is end-stopped with a rhyme.

Writing about 'My Grandfather's Garden'

D In *My Grandfather's Garden*, the speaker focuses more on his memories of the time he spent in the garden than on his memories of his grandfather, which shows how important this place was to him.

E The speaker describes his grandfather's shed using the metaphor of a 'hollow socket', suggesting that it feels empty because his grandfather is not in it any more, which highlights the speaker's feeling of loss and emptiness at his death.

F In *My Grandfather's Garden*, the use of enjambment creates a slow pace and a reflective mood that emphasise the huge impact of his grandfather's death on the speaker.

Writing about 'Poem'

G In *Poem*, the speaker contrasts the good and bad aspects of the man's life, for example how the man 'praised' his wife but also 'punched her in the face'.

H However, the bad aspects are described after the good, using slang and aggressive language choices, which make the bad aspects stand out more than the good.

I In *Poem*, the use of rhyme and end-stopped lines create a strong rhythm, a fast pace and a tone that suggest the speaker does not think any of these things are very important.

ⓐ Which sentences focus on a **key idea**? Label ✎ them **K**.

ⓑ Which sentences focus on the **poets' choices** of language, form or structure? Label ✎ them **C**.

ⓒ Which sentences would you include in a paragraph comparing the two poems? Tick ✓ them.

ⓓ Number ✎ the sentences you have ticked to show how you would sequence them in a paragraph.

Comparing poems

To write an effective comparison of two poems, you need to:

- identify and compare the key ideas in the poems
- develop your comparison, exploring and comparing the poets' choices of language, form and structure
- structure each paragraph of your response to make a careful, developed comparison of the two poems.

Now look at this exam-style question, which you saw at the start of the unit.

Exam-style question

Compare the ways the writers present someone's death in *My Grandfather's Garden* and *Poem*.

In your answer you should compare:

- the ideas in the poems
- the poets' use of language
- the poets' use of form.

Use **evidence** from the poems to support your **comparison**.

(20 marks)

Read the paragraph below, written by a student in response to this exam-style question.

> The poets create very different impressions of the people who have died. In *My Grandfather's Garden*, the impression is created of a quiet, organised man who 'kept order' in his garden and because he is not really described it seems like you might not even notice him. In *Poem* though, the man's life is listed in lots of detail, making him seem violent and dishonest. He once 'slippered' his daughter and 'punched his wife'. The poet emphasises how unfair and horrible the man is by showing why he did this – his wife laughed and his daughter told just one lie. Both poets use the form of the poem to add to these impressions: in *Poem* the rhyme and repetition of 'And' create a fast, aggressive pace, reflecting the aggression of the man described, whereas the enjambment and irregular lines in *My Grandfather's Garden* create a quiet, reflective mood as the speaker remembers his quiet grandfather and the time he spent in his garden.

① Annotate the paragraph, underlining Ⓐ and labelling ✏️ A to H the parts of the paragraph in which this student has achieved the key features below.

Focusing on both poems	Focusing on *My Grandfather's Garden*	Focusing on *Poem*
A identifies a significant similarity or difference B compares poets' choices	C identifies a key idea D evidence to support key idea E comments on effect of poet's choices	F identifies a key idea G evidence to support key idea H comments on effect of poet's choices

Your turn!

You are now going to **plan and write your response** to the exam-style question.

Exam-style question

Compare the ways the writers present someone's death in *My Grandfather's Garden* and *Poem*.

In your answer you should compare:
- the ideas in the poems
- the poets' use of language
- the poets' use of form.

Use **evidence** from the poems to support your **comparison**.   (20 marks)

(1) Use the space below to plan **three paragraphs** in response to the question.

(a) Note (✎) **three** similarities or differences in the ways the poets present their thoughts and feelings after someone has died. Compare the **key ideas** and the poets' choices of language, form and structure in the poems.

(b) For each similarity or difference, note (✎) relevant evidence from each poem. This could be a quotation, a description of the poem's form or structure, a poetic device, etc.

(c) Annotate (✎) your evidence, noting the effect of the poets' language, form and structure choices.

Similarity or Difference	Evidence: *My Grandfather's Garden*	Evidence: *Poem*

(2) Now write (✎) your response to the exam-style question above on paper.

Review your skills

Check up

Review your response to the exam-style question on page 63. Tick ✓ the column to show how well you think you have done each of the following.

	Not quite ✓	Nearly there ✓	Got it! ✓
identified significant similarities and/or differences	☐	☐	☐
explored the poets' choices of language, form and structure	☐	☐	☐
structured my paragraphs effectively	☐	☐	☐

Need more practice?

Here is another exam-style question, this time relating to a comparison of *My Grandfather's Garden*, which can be found on page 58 and *When You Are Old* on page 73.

Exam-style question

Compare the ways the writers present feelings of loss in *My Grandfather's Garden* and *When You Are Old*.

In your answer you should compare:
• the ideas in the poems
• the poets' use of language
• the poets' use of form.

Use **evidence** from the poems to support your **comparison**.   (20 marks)

Plan and write 🖉 your response to this exam-style question. You'll find some suggested points to refer to in the Answers section.

How confident do you feel about each of these **skills?** Colour 🖉 in the bars.

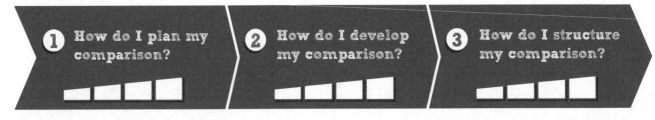

1 How do I plan my comparison?	2 How do I develop my comparison?	3 How do I structure my comparison?

⑨ Expressing your ideas clearly and precisely

This unit will help you to express your response to unseen poems as clearly and precisely as possible. The skills you will build are to:

- select vocabulary to express your ideas precisely
- link your ideas to express them clearly
- extend your sentences to develop ideas more fully.

In the exam you will face a question like the one below. At the end of the unit you will **write one paragraph** in response to the question, focusing on *On Children*. You will then have an opportunity to explore the second poem and compare them both.

Exam-style question

Compare the ways the writers present being a parent in *On Children* and *Mother to Son*.

In your answer you should compare:
- the ideas in the poems
- the poets' use of language
- the poets' use of form.

Use **evidence** from the poems to support your **comparison**.   (20 marks)

Before you tackle the question you will work through three key questions in the **skills boosts** to help you develop a critical writing style.

> **①** How do I choose vocabulary which expresses my ideas precisely?
>
> **②** How can I link my ideas to express them more clearly?
>
> **③** How can I extend my sentences to develop my ideas more fully?

Read the poem on the next page. In Paper 2, Section B, Part 2 of your English Literature exam, you will compare **two** unseen poems.

As you read the poem, think about: ⊘

who the speaker in the poem is talking to	the key ideas and advice the speaker gives the reader	why the reader might want or need the speaker's advice.

On Children

Your children are not your children.
They are the sons and daughters of Life's longing for itself.
They come through you but not from you,
And though they are with you yet they belong not to you.

5   You may give them your love but not your thoughts,
For they have their own thoughts.
You may house their bodies but not their souls,
For their souls dwell in the house of tomorrow,
which you cannot visit, not even in your dreams.
10   You may strive to be like them,
but seek not to make them like you.
For life goes not backward nor **tarries** with yesterday.

You are the bows from which your children
as living arrows are sent forth.
15   The archer sees the mark upon the path of the infinite,
and He bends you with His might
that His arrows may go swift and far.
Let your bending in the archer's hand be for gladness;
For even as He loves the arrow that flies,
20   so He loves also the bow that is stable.

Khalil Gibran

tarries: remains, waits around, delays leaving somewhere

(1) In the table below, note ✎ some of the advice given in the poem.

What parents *should not do*	What parents *should do*
•	• ....
•	• ....
•	• ....

(2) Write ✎ **one** or **two** sentences summing up the key ideas in the poem.

....

....

....

....

1 How do I choose vocabulary which expresses my ideas precisely?

When you write and review your response to a poem, or compare two poems, think about synonyms you could use to make your description of the poet's intention and choices more precise.

synonym: a word with a similar meaning, e.g. large, big, huge, vast, etc.

① Look again at the poem *On Children* on page 66. Read it aloud or, as you read it to yourself, try to hear your voice 'inside your head'.

How would you describe the **pace** of the poem? Circle Ⓐ **one** or **two** words below, or add ✏ your own ideas. You could use a thesaurus to help you.

slow	lethargic		regular	even		fast	hurried
hesitant	plodding		measured	steady		rapid	energetic

② How would you describe the **mood** of the poem? Circle Ⓐ **one** or **two** words below, or add ✏ your own ideas. You could use a thesaurus to help you.

angry	assertive	commanding	calm	reflective	anxious	happy	chaotic
aggressive	authoritative	certain	confident	melancholy	tense	joyous	excited

③ Look again at your answers to questions ① and ②. Write ✏ **one** or **two** sentences commenting on the pace and mood of the poem *On Children*.

....

....

....

④ How would you describe the **poet's intention** in the poem? Write ✏ **one** or **two** sentences using the phrases below.

| The poet's intention is to: |

| persuade the reader to | describe | create the impression that |

| explore ideas of | explore and express feelings of | take a surprisingly different look at |

| invite the reader to | think differently about | explore a significant moment in their life when |

....

....

....

....

② How can I link my ideas to express them more clearly?

You can use conjunctions and adverbials to link your ideas, helping you to express your views more clearly and fluently.

Conjunctions			
and	but	when	after
before	although	because	whereas

Adverbials		
also	therefore	similarly
	in the same way	however

① Look at the conjunctions and adverbials above. Add ✎ each one to the table below, to show the kinds of idea they can link.

	link similar ideas	link contrasting ideas	link explanations or consequences	indicate time or place
Conjunctions that can...				
Adverbials that can...				

② Rewrite ✎ the sentences below by:

EITHER

• using a **conjunction** to join the two sentences and **form one sentence**

OR:

• adding an **adverbial** to the second sentence **without joining them**.

For example:

Children have their own thoughts. Parents do not need to give them theirs.

(Because) children have their own thoughts, parents do not need to give them theirs.

Children have their own thoughts. (Therefore,) parents do not need to give them theirs.

a   The speaker suggests that parents should not treat their children as possessions.

He says, 'they belong not to you'.

....

....

b   The speaker suggests that parents should be loving.

They should not try to control or dominate their children.

....

....

c   The poet contrasts what parents think with what children really are.

He contrasts what parents should do with what they should not do.

....

....

③ How can I extend my sentences to develop my ideas more fully?

You can extend your sentences, and develop your ideas, by using:
- a present participle: a verb ending '-ing'
- the pronoun 'which'.

① You can use 'which' or a present participle to avoid repeatedly beginning sentences with 'This suggests…' or 'This shows…'. For example:

> Children are compared to 'living arrows'. (This) suggests they fly quickly and purposefully.

> Children are compared to 'living arrows', (which) suggests they fly quickly and purposefully.

> Children are compared to 'living arrows', (suggesting) they fly quickly and purposefully.

Change ✐ the sentences below into single sentences, using a present participle or 'which'.

ⓐ The speaker says that parents may 'house' their children's bodies. This highlights the role of parents in providing food and warmth for them.

....

....

ⓑ The speaker says that parents cannot 'visit' their children's souls 'even in your dreams'. This implies how different children and parents are.

....

....

② You can sometimes replace a conjunction with a present participle. For example:

> Parents are like a bow (because they send) their children out into the world.

> Parents are like a bow, (sending) their children out into the world.

Circle Ⓐ the conjunction in the sentences below. Replace ✐ the conjunction with a present participle.

ⓐ The poem shows how important it is to give children freedom and allow them to be themselves.

....

....

ⓑ The speaker highlights how parents feel the need to give children their thoughts and make them think the same as they do.

....

....

Expressing your ideas clearly and precisely

To express your ideas clearly and precisely, you can:

- select vocabulary that expresses your ideas precisely
- link your ideas using conjunctions, present participles, etc. to develop and express them clearly.

Now look at this exam-style question, which you saw at the start of the unit.

Exam-style question

Compare the ways the writers present being a parent in *On Children* and *Mother to Son*.

In your answer you should compare:
- the ideas in the poems
- the poets' use of language
- the poets' use of form.

Use **evidence** from the poems to support your **comparison**. (20 marks)

Look at this short paragraph from one student's response to the exam-style question.

> In On Children, the speaker wants to get parents to think about how they treat their children. He describes parents as a bow that fires an arrow. He describes their children as the arrow. This shows how important the parents' job is. Without parents, children could not 'fly'. This shows that children need to be separate from their parents.

① **a** Underline Ⓐ **at least three** examples of vocabulary which could be more precise.

b Note 🖉 down in the margin **at least two** alternative vocabulary choices for each one.

c Highlight 🖉 any of the sentences which you feel should be linked or developed to improve the clarity and precision of the writing.

d Write 🖉 an improved version of this paragraph, either by adjusting the text above or by rewriting it in the space below.

....

....

....

....

....

....

....

Your turn!

You are now going to **write one paragraph** in response to the exam-style question focusing on *On Children*.

Exam-style question

Compare the ways the writers present being a parent in *On Children* and *Mother to Son*.

In your answer you should compare:
- the ideas in the poems
- the poets' use of language
- the poets' use of form.

Use **evidence** from the poems to support your **comparison**. (20 marks)

(1) In your response, you could explore one or more of the key features of the poem. Add 🖉 some ideas about *On Children* to **at least three** of the headings below.

? **The poet's intention**

? **The key ideas in the poem**

? **Some of the poet's choices of language and/or poetic devices and their effect**

? **The poet's choice of form and structure and its effect**

? **The pace and mood of the poem**

(2) Now add 🖉 relevant evidence to support each of your ideas.

(3) Review the ideas and evidence you have noted. Which will you include and link in the paragraph you are going to write in response to the exam-style question above? Tick ✓ them.

(4) Now write 🖉 **one** paragraph on paper in response to the exam-style question, focusing on *On Children* **only**.

Remember to:
- choose your vocabulary carefully
- think about ways in which you can link your ideas to develop and express them clearly and precisely.

Review your skills

	Not quite ✓	Nearly there ✓	Got it! ✓
selected precise vocabulary	☐	☐	☐
linked and developed my ideas clearly and precisely using conjunctions, adverbials, present participles, etc.	☐	☐	☐

Need more practice?

You can EITHER:

1. Look again at your paragraph about *On Children*, written in preparation for a response to the exam-style question on page 71. Rewrite ✏ it, experimenting with different vocabulary choices and sentence structures, linking your ideas in different ways. Which are most effective in expressing your ideas clearly and precisely?

AND/OR:

2. Write ✏ a **second** paragraph about *On Children*, using some more of the ideas you noted on page 71. Remember to focus closely on your vocabulary choices and sentence structures to express your ideas as clearly and precisely as possible.

Comparison practice

Now write ✏ **one** paragraph in response to the exam-style question, **comparing** *On Children* and *Mother to Son* by Langston Hughes on page 75. Focus on **expressing your ideas as clearly and precisely as possible.**

How confident do you feel about each of these **skills?** Colour ✏ in the bars.

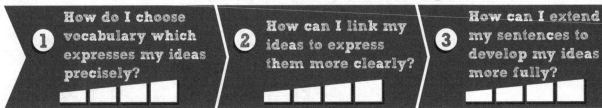

1. How do I choose vocabulary which expresses my ideas precisely?
2. How can I link my ideas to express them more clearly?
3. How can I extend my sentences to develop my ideas more fully?

More practice texts

When You Are Old

When you are old and grey and full of sleep,
And nodding by the fire, take down this book,
And slowly read, and dream of the soft look
Your eyes had once, and of their shadows deep;

5   How many loved your moments of glad grace,
And loved your beauty with love false or true,
But one man loved the pilgrim soul in you,
And loved the sorrows of your changing face;

And bending down beside the glowing bars,
10 Murmur, a little sadly, how Love fled
And paced upon the mountains overhead
And hid his face amid a crowd of stars.

William Butler Yeats

The rooms were mirrors
for that luminous face,
the morning windows ferned
with cold. Outside
5   a level world of snow.
Voiceless birds in the trees
like notes in the books
in the piano stool.
She let us suck top-of-the-milk
10 burst from the bottles like corks.
Then wrapped shapeless
we stumped to the park
between the parapets of snow
in the wake of the shovellers,
15 cardboard rammed in the tines of garden forks.
The lake was an empty rink
and I stepped out,
pushing my sister first
onto its creaking floor.
20 When I brought her home,
shivering, wailing, soaked,
they thought me a hero.
But I still wake at night,
to hear the Snow Queen's knuckles crack,
25 black water running fingers through the ice.

Gillian Clarke

Mother to Son

Well, son, I'll tell you:
Life for me ain't been no crystal stair.
It's had tacks in it,
And splinters,
5   And boards torn up,
And places with no carpet on the floor—
Bare.
But all the time
I'se been a-climbin' on,
10 And reachin' landin's,
And turnin' corners,
And sometimes goin' in the dark
Where there ain't been no light.
So boy, don't you turn back.
15 Don't you set down on the steps
'Cause you finds it's kinder hard.
Don't you fall now—
For I'se still goin', honey,
I'se still climbin',
20 And life for me ain't been no crystal stair.

Langston Hughes

A Letter in October

Dawn comes later and later now,
and I, who only a month ago
could sit with coffee every morning
watching the light walk down the hill
5   to the edge of the pond and place
a doe there, shyly drinking,

then see the light step out upon
the water, sowing reflections
to either side—a garden
10   of trees that grew as if by magic—
now see no more than my face,
mirrored by darkness, pale and odd,

startled by time. While I slept,
night in its thick winter jacket
15   bridled the doe with a twist
of wet leaves and led her away,
then brought its black horse with harness
that creaked like a cricket, and turned

the water garden under. I woke,
20   and at the waiting window found
the curtains open to my open face;
beyond me, darkness. And I,
who only wished to keep looking out,
must now keep looking in.

Ted Kooser

Answers

Unit 1

Page 2

② A Jasmine, Gunpowder, Assam, Earl Grey and Ceylon are different types of tea. The phrase 'I love tea's names' is a useful clue.

    B Mount Wu-Yi is a mountain in China where tea is grown. The phrase 'harvest the slopes' offers a clue.

Page 3

① ⓐ Details could include: the speaker looking happy, her lover, a teapot, etc.

    ⓑ For example: The speaker is in love and enjoys making tea for her lover.

    ⓓ For example: 'I like pouring your tea'; 'I am your lover, smitten, straining your tea.'

Page 4

① ⓐ For example: love, making tea

② ⓐ For example:

    Tea: Assam, Ceylon, china, cup, cupped, Earl Grey, fragrant, Gunpowder, harvest, Jasmine, leaves, liquid, milk, Mount Wu-Yi, pot, pouring, sip, slopes, straining, sugar, sweetest, tea, tipping

    Love: eyes, half-smile, hands, heart, lips, love, lover, smitten, soul

③ ⓐ I, your, it, your, you're, I, your, you, you, your, I, I, I, your, your, I, I, you, I, it's, you, I, your, your

    ⓑ For example: The most frequent pronoun used is 'you'/'your', followed closely by 'I' and then 'it', suggesting that the poet ('I') is oblivious to almost everything except the object of her poem – her new lover ('you'). Very little from the outside world intrudes on their love in the poem, except their mutual enjoyment of tea.

Page 5

① The speaker directly addresses her lover, talking about her lover's fondness for tea, and her happiness in making tea for her lover.

② The quotation suggests that the couple have not been together long, but that the speaker is entirely absorbed by her deep feelings of love.

③ The overriding impression is of the speaker's love. Little is revealed about her lover, other than their love of tea.

Page 6

② D and E are least relevant to the focus of the question.

Page 8

Sample Need more practice responses:

- The speaker imagines someone he once loved has grown old.
- Suggests many admired this person for her physical beauty, but none loved them as deeply as the speaker.
- The speaker imagines this person is alone and lonely now love has 'fled'.

- Suggests the speaker may have feelings of bitterness; perhaps his love for this person was not recognised or returned.

Sample Comparison practice responses:

'Tea':

- Focuses on a current relationship.
- Focuses on strong feelings of love and happiness.

'When You Are Old':

- Focuses on a past relationship.
- Focuses on lost love and feelings of bitterness.

Unit 2

Page 10

① ⓐ For example: four children go to a beach: Maggie finds a shell; Milly finds a starfish; Molly is chased by a crab; May finds a stone.

    ⓑ For example: The poem focuses on the experiences of four children at the beach.

Page 11

① For example: The words 'beach' and 'play' suggest the poem will describe four children happily playing at the seaside. It creates a positive image of fun and friendship.

② For example: 'troubles' suggests Maggie may be troubled in some way; 'befriended' could suggest that Milly is lonely and finds it difficult to make friends; 'chased' suggests Molly may be fearful or nervous; 'alone' suggests May is familiar with loneliness.

③ There is a surprising connection made between the initial image of a group of children on a beach, and the four separate images of the children as isolated individuals, focusing on the difficulties they face.

Page 12

① ⓐ For example: positive, optimistic, happy

    ⓑ 'beach'; 'play'

② ⓐ For example: unsettling, unsettled

    ⓑ 'chased'; 'horrible'; 'alone'

Page 13

① ⓐ For example:

    A. 'went down to the beach (to play...'

    B. 'couldn't remember her troubles', 'befriended a stranded star', 'chased', 'alone'

    C. Verses 2–5 focus on each child, one at a time.

    D. 'troubles', 'chased', 'alone'

    E. 'couldn't remember her troubles', 'chased'

    ⓑ A is the least developed; E is the most developed, giving the broadest response to the poem.

② ⓐ For example:

    Our responses to nature – and to life – reveal something about ourselves.

    We can lose ourselves, and find out what we are truly like, by interacting with the natural world.

Page 14

1. **a** Both
   b Student A
   c Student B

Page 16

Sample Need more practice responses:

- The speaker and her sister are presented as a pair, referred to as 'us' and 'we', until the accident.
- Childhood is a time of excitement and danger.
- The mood changes from excitement to dramatic disaster.

Sample Comparison practice responses:

maggie and milly and molly and may:

- Children are presented as individuals, playing separately.
- Childhood is a time of excitement and danger.
- The mood changes from positive to unsettling.

Legend:

- The speaker and her sister are presented as a pair, referred to as 'us' and 'we', until the accident.
- Childhood is a time of excitement and danger.
- The mood changes from excitement to dramatic disaster.

Unit 3

Page 18

1. Get up, eat cereal, walk the dog, work, lie down with their mate, eat dinner, sleep.

Page 19

1. **a** Time
   b 'I got out of bed', 'cereal', 'All morning', 'At noon', 'ate dinner', 'slept', 'another day'
   c The poet describes the events in a typical day of her life from waking up until going to sleep.
2. **a** The last two lines: lines 25–6
   b A sudden reversal: the speaker effectively dismisses the happiness of the preceding lines by sharply shifting her focus to a different, potentially less pleasant future.

Page 20

1. The poem is mainly focused on the thoughts and feelings of the speaker.
2. For example:
   - the actual past: 'I got out of bed'
   - a possible past: 'It might have been otherwise'
   - a definite future: 'it will be otherwise'
3. **a** 'It might have been otherwise.'
   b For example:
   The repetition emphasises her awareness of how her life could have turned out differently, implying that she feels fortunate.
4. **a/b** The speaker contrasts her life now with her life in the future, highlighting that she expects significant change.

Page 21

1–5 All responses are potentially valid.

Page 22

identifies a key idea in the poem	The speaker gives a strong impression that she thinks she is very fortunate in her life.
supports key idea with evidence	for example, it begins when she 'got out of bed' and then 'ate cereal' and it ends as she 'slept in a bed' ...for example, she has 'two strong legs', suggesting she is healthy, and she has 'silver candlesticks', suggesting she has wealth.
identifies a structural element or feature	The poem is structured around the events of a typical day in her life... After each of these events, she repeats the phrase 'It might have been otherwise'.
comments on the effect of the poet's structural choice	Each of these events highlights a positive aspect of her life:
comments on how the effect of the structural choice supports the poet's intention	The poem's structure and the use of repetition strongly imply how grateful she feels that everything she does and has in her life makes her happy and comfortable and that she can choose how she spends and enjoys her days.

Page 24

Sample Need more practice responses:

- Focuses on the speaker's past and present and her son's future: written in the first person, directly addressed to her son.
- Contrasts image of life as a 'crystal stair' with the reality of her life: 'tacks', 'splinters', 'boards torn up', 'no carpet'.
- Repetition of 'life for me ain't been no crystal stair' in final line emphasises speaker's key idea: her life has been difficult.

Sample Comparison practice responses:

Mother to Son:

- Focuses on past, then present, then future.
- Repetition in final line suggests past and future will not differ.

Otherwise:

- Focuses on present, then future.
- Repetition of 'It might have been otherwise' contrasted with 'it will be otherwise' in final line suggests the present and the future will differ.

Unit 4

Page 26

1. For example, possible impressions include:

   the city: a: dilapidated: 'abandoned to crisp packets and cans'. **b:** busy: 'men and women are lost in transactions'

   people who live in the city: a: focused on making money: 'the deal is done'. **b:** isolated: 'a new mother stands on her doorstep and blinks'

the lilacs that grow in the city: a: resilient: 'in all these places the city lilacs are pushing / their cones of blossom into the spring'. **b:** beautiful: 'sweet, wild perfume'

Page 27

① **a** the city

    b For example: ugly, dirty, miserable

② **b** For example: 'crack-haunted', 'sour', 'wheelie bin'

③ **a** The people in the city

    b For example: busy, isolated, cold, miserable

    c For example: 'men', 'urgent', 'girls shiver', 'new mother', 'blinks'

Page 28

① All are arguable.

② For example:

    rich: wealth, fertility, growth

    sweet: appealing, delicious, productive

    poor: poverty, infertility, low quality

    starved: mistreated, thin, weak

③ For example: The description 'sour earth' suggests the soil in the city is spoilt and rotten and that nothing can grow there.

④ For example: 'urgent' suggests fast-paced, desperate, anxious; 'shiver' suggests cold, fear, discomfort.

Page 29

① **a** vague: E

    describe: A

    b effect: C, D

    intention: B

② vague: D

    describe: B

    effect: A

    intention: C, E

Page 30

identifies a key idea in the poem	The poet then contrasts her description of a broken and neglected city with her description of the lilacs that grow there.
identifies a significant language choice	She describes the lilacs 'pushing' their way into the city
comments on the connotations/effect of language choice	which suggests their strength and power as though it takes a massive effort to squeeze into this crowded and unwelcoming place
comments on how language choice supports the poet's intention	giving the impression of nature as powerful and something that will always survive. This strength of nature makes the city seem a better place, as though there is life and strength, not just loneliness and decay.

Page 32

Sample Need more practice responses:

- Vivid, appealing description of life of late summer: 'light', 'reflections', 'garden … magic' contrasts with negative images of autumn's lifeless, cold, wet darkness: 'thick winter jacket', 'wet leaves', 'darkness'.

- Seasonal changes in nature force the speaker to focus on himself, reflected in darkness: 'pale and odd'.

Sample Comparison practice responses:

City Lilacs:

- Positive language contrasts the power of the natural world: 'city lilacs … pushing / their cones of blossom into the spring', 'sweet, wild perfume', with negative images of city life: 'crack-haunted alleys', 'sour earth'.

A Letter in October:

- Contrasts positive language describing light and life of late summer with negative language describing darkness and cold of October.

Unit 5

Page 34

① **a** / **b** 'A regularly repeated sequence of activities' is implied particularly through the repetition of 'as it does each day' in the final stanza.

Page 35

① For example:

    A: 'splashed': onomatopoeia; 'splashed', 'swaying', 'stems': alliteration

    B: 'humps of the honeybees': alliteration and assonance

② Adds emphasis; makes the description more vivid; you can hear and see what the poet is describing, giving greater sensory immediacy to the image.

③ **b** For example: The soft alliterative sounds in these lines create a peaceful, quiet mood suggesting the sound of splashing water / a gentle breeze.

④ Adds emphasis; links two words to highlight a surprising image.

Page 36

① 'splashed': metaphor

② For example: The image gives the light a feeling of fluidity, refreshing and giving life to the plants.

③ **a** For example: romance, affection, intimacy, gentle

    b The image suggests the gentle, loving affection of the light landing on the roses.

Page 37

① **a** vague: C, D

    describe: A

    b effect: B

    intention: E

② vague: B

    describe: A

    effect: C, D

    intention: E

Page 38

identifies a key idea in the poem	*In the second part of the poem, the speaker goes into his house to finish a poem about his experience in the garden …describes the place he goes to write the poem in very negative terms.*
identifies a poetic device	*He uses the metaphor of a 'cell' to describe it… He describes his view of a compost heap as a 'steamy old stinkpile'. The alliteration of the letter 's' in this description…*
comments on the effect of a poetic device	*…suggesting it is small and like being in prison. …almost suggests the hiss of the stinking fumes wafting up from the compost heap and floating in through his window.*
comments on how poetic devices support the poet's intention	*Both of these images use poetic devices to emphasise the difference between his experience inside the house, writing about the beauty of nature, compared with his experience outside the house, actually enjoying the beauty of nature.*

Page 40

Sample Need more practice responses:

* Light personified: 'watching the light walk down the hill'
* Darkness personified in opposition to light: 'brought its black horse', 'turned / the water garden under'
* Onomatopoeia/alliteration/simile of 'creaked like a cricket' creates powerful image of darkness.

Sample Comparison practice responses:

The Round:

* The natural world/light presented as life-giving, creating a peaceful, quiet mood.

A Letter in October:

* The natural world in autumn presented as the loss of light/ beauty to the power of darkness.

Unit 6

Page 42

① Last day of summer: 'the day the summer went', 'wind and dark still forage at my door'
② Stanzas 1–4
③ Stanzas 5–8
④ A, C, E (e.g. 'road… toad'; 'happened… opened'), G ('I saw…')

Page 43

① A, B: regular form; C, D, E, F: free verse
② For example: The use of repetition at the start of stanzas 1–4 emphasises the impression of a series of snapshots. This pattern of repetition and description ends, and the mood changes in stanzas 5–8 as the poet reflects on what she has seen.

Page 44

① ⓐ Taking out the rhyme changes the mood.
Changing the rhythm changes the mood, pace and emphasis.

ⓑ The regular rhythm and use of rhyme help to create a calm, even pace, suggesting a very reflective mood.

② For example:

The use of enjambment in the last four stanzas:

* changes the pace of the poem, making it faster.
* changes the mood of the poem, making it more anxious / less reflective.
* gives emphasis to the phrase 'or hate'.

Page 45

① For example:

In the first part of the poem:

the poet uses a regular stanza form | to create a series of scenes or snapshots

the poet uses a regular rhythm and rhyme | to create a regular, even pace | to create a reflective, thoughtful mood

In the second part of the poem:

the poet uses enjambment | to suggest the patterns of everyday speech | to create a faster pace | to suggest that the speaker's thoughts are suddenly racing.

② For example:

A: free verse, no regular rhythm, enjambment, short lines, no rhyme, a faster pace

M: a regular stanza form, a regular rhythm, longer lines, some rhyme and half rhyme, a slower pace

C: a regular stanza form, a regular rhythm, short lines, some rhyme and half rhyme, a faster pace

Page 46

① ⓐ Students A, B and C have all identified significant features of form.

ⓑ Student A's comments are vague and undeveloped. Comments on the 'flow' of a poem, and evaluation of the effect as 'quite effective' without explanation of how or why, are largely meaningless.

Students B and C effectively develop their comments on the effect of the poet's use of form and the contribution to the poet's intention.

Page 48

Sample Need more practice responses:

* Regular line length/stanza form and enjambment create a slower pace and reflective mood.
* Contrasting repetition of 'looking out', 'looking in' mirrors the change from light to darkness, summer to autumn.

Sample Comparison practice responses:

Postcard:

* Short stanzas, rhyme and regular rhythm create a series of separate images or 'snapshots'.
* Final end-stopped line, contrasting with enjambment, highlights the final image of 'wind and dark'.

A Letter in October:

* Longer stanzas and enjambment create a reflective mood as the speaker observes the changing season.
* Final end-stopped line, contrasting with enjambment, highlights the final image of the speaker's reflection in his window 'looking in'.

Unit 7

Page 50

(1) All responses are valid if supported by a valid explanation.

Page 51

(1) For example: The speaker and his lover eat strawberries on a hot day and are consumed by passion.

(2) (a) For example: 'your knees held in mine'

(3) (a) For example: strawberries are red and heart-shaped, reflecting the theme of love/passion.

(b) For example: The image reflects the closeness of the couple.

(4) (a) For example: The ideas in the poem are presented as brief 'snapshots' that cumulatively build an image of the scene, and the speaker's relationship with his lover.

(b) For example: The final line/stanza is given additional emphasis.

Page 52

(1) For example: This could suggest the speaker's lover is helpless in his arms because of their love for him. It makes his lover seem vulnerable but comfortable in this situation.

(2) For example: The poet's choice of language and structure emphasises the power of the sun. This shows the strength of the speaker's passion because it distracts him from the fierce heat of the sun.

Page 53

(1) (a) weather, love and passion

(b) weather: B, E

love and passion: A, C, D, F

(2) (a) B

(b) C, D, F

Page 54

(1) All are arguably relevant; however, point 'C' is not immediately relevant, and point 'D' focuses more on the speaker's lover's feelings than on the speaker's.

(2) All are arguably relevant.

(3) Annotations to A, B, E and F show the most developed comments on the poet's choices.

Page 56

Sample Need more practice responses:

- Focus on faded physical beauty: 'the soft look / Your eyes had once', 'glad grace'.

- Love can be 'false or true'.

- The speaker loved this person's 'pilgrim soul' and her 'sorrows', suggesting true love goes beyond happiness and physical beauty.

- Love is personified: it 'fled' and 'hid his face', suggesting love can be lost.

Sample Comparison practice responses:

Strawberries:

- Focuses on an afternoon of passion.

- Focuses on the happiness of a close relationship.

- Suggests love is more powerful than any other thought or feeling.

When You Are Old:

- Focuses on the impact of love on an entire lifetime.

- Explores the feelings of a rejected lover.

- Suggests feelings of love can be 'false or true'.

Unit 8

Page 58

(1) (b) For example:

My Grandfather's Garden: 'Where he kept order with hoe prods' suggests a man who cared for his garden methodically and carefully; 'the house and garden following him out of my life' suggests the speaker feels his loss keenly.

Poem: 'And praised his wife for every meal she made / And once, for laughing, punched her in the face' suggests this man's unpredictable behaviour: a seemingly loving and grateful man with an unforgivably violent, irrational temper.

Page 59

(1) For example:

Both poems are about someone who has died.

However, *My Grandfather's Garden* focuses on the memories of the speaker in the poem, suggesting feelings of loss and sadness at the death of his quiet, patient grandfather,

whereas in *Poem* the speaker describes both the good and bad things that an anonymous man did in his life, suggesting his violence and dishonesty, but the speaker expresses no emotions at his death.

(2) (a) A: b, d, e

B: a

C: c, f

(b) All are differences.

Page 60

(1) (a) 'kept order'; 'punched her in the face'

(b) For example:

In *My Grandfather's Garden*, the speaker presents his grandfather as an organised man who spent his time working in his garden to grow fruit and vegetables.

However, in *Poem*, the speaker creates the impression that the man who has died was aggressive and short-tempered, with little respect for his wife.

(2) For example:

In *My Grandfather's Garden* the poet uses repetition of the word 'Where' to emphasise the importance of this place whereas in *Poem* the poet uses repetition of the word 'And' to emphasise the different events in a life.

In *My Grandfather's Garden* the poet uses enjambment to create a slow pace and a quiet reflective mood. However, in *Poem*, the poet uses rhyme and end-stopped lines to create a fast pace and an abrupt, aggressive mood.

Page 61

(1) a A, B, D, G focus on key ideas.

b C, E, F, H, I focus on the poets' choices.

c All are valid.

d For example: A, B, D, E, G, H, C, F, I

Page 62

(1) A The poets create very different impressions of the people who have died.

B Both poets use the form of the poem to add to these impressions:

...in *Poem* the rhyme and repetition of 'And' create a fast, aggressive pace, reflecting the aggression of the man described, whereas the enjambment and irregular lines in *My Grandfather's Garden* create a quiet, reflective mood as the speaker remembers his quiet grandfather and the time he spent in his garden.

C In 'My Grandfather's Garden', the impression is created of a quiet, organised man

D who 'kept order' in his garden and because he is not really described

E it seems like you might not even notice him.

F In 'Poem' though, the man's life is listed in lots of detail, making him seem violent and dishonest.

G He once 'slippered' his daughter and 'punched his wife'.

H The poet emphasises how unfair and horrible the man is by showing why he did this – his wife laughed and his daughter told just one lie.

Page 64

Sample Need more practice responses:

My Grandfather's Garden:

* Series of vivid memories of time spent in this garden, looking back over the past.
* Focuses on the speaker's thoughts and feelings.
* Highlights the speaker's sense of loss: 'the house and garden following him out of my life', 'hollow socket'.

When You Are Old:

* An imagined future, inviting a former love to look back over the past.
* Focuses on the imagined thoughts and feelings of the former lover.
* Highlights the speaker's feelings of loss: 'how Love fled'.

Unit 9

Page 66

(1) For example:

What parents should not do: try to make children think the same way as them; try to restrict or contain their children's 'souls'; try to make their children like themselves.

What parents should do: give children their love; 'house their bodies'; try to be like their children.

(2) Parents should love and nurture their children but not try to control or mould them.

Page 67

(1) For example: regular, measured

(2) For example: confident, authoritative

(3) For example: The poet creates a regular, measured pace resulting in a confident, authoritative mood.

(4) For example: The poet's intention is to persuade the reader to think differently about the role of being a parent.

Page 68

(1)

	link similar ideas	link contrasting ideas	link explanations or consequences	indicate time or place
Conjunctions that can...	and	but although whereas	because	when after before
Adverbials that can...	also similarly in the same way	however	therefore	–

② For example:

a The speaker suggests that parents should not treat their children as possessions <u>because/when</u> he says, 'they belong not to you'.

b The speaker suggests that parents should be loving <u>but</u> they should not try to control or dominate their children.

The speaker suggests that parents should be loving. <u>However,</u> they should not try to control or dominate their children.

c The poet contrasts what parents think with what children really are, <u>and</u> what parents should do with what they should not do.

The poet contrasts what parents think with what children really are. <u>Similarly,</u> he contrasts what parents should do with what they should not do.

Page 69

① **a** The speaker says that parents may 'house' their children's bodies, <u>which highlights/highlighting</u> the role of parents in providing food and warmth for them.

b The speaker says that parents cannot 'visit' their children's souls 'even in your dreams', <u>which implies/implying</u> how different children and parents are.

② **a** The poem shows how important it is to give children freedom, ~~and~~ <u>allowing</u> them to be themselves.

b The speaker highlights how parents feel the need to give children their thoughts, ~~and~~ <u>making</u> them think the same as they do.

Page 70

① **d** For example:

In *On Children*, the speaker wants to ~~get~~ <u>encourage/persuade</u> parents to ~~think about~~ <u>consider/evaluate</u> how they treat their children. He describes parents as a bow that fires an arrow. ~~He describes~~ <u>and</u> their children as the arrow. ~~This shows,~~ showing how ~~important~~ <u>vital/essential</u> the parents' job is <u>because,</u> without parents, children could not 'fly'. This ~~shows~~ <u>suggests/implies</u> that children need to be separate from their parents.

Page 72

Sample Comparison practice responses:

'On Children':

* The speaker focuses on how parents should treat children.

* The speaker contrasts how parents may *want* to treat their children with how he feels they *should* treat their children.

* The speaker uses the metaphor of a bow and arrow to highlight the roles of parent and child.

'Mother to Son':

* The speaker focuses on how children can learn from a parent, presenting herself as a role model.

* The speaker highlights similarities between the challenges of her life and those her son is facing or will face.

* The speaker uses the metaphor of stairs to highlight life as an uphill climb for both parent and child.

Notes